SAI SPEED MATH ACAI

MW00399017

ABACUS MIND MATH

Excel at Mind Math with Soroban, a Japanese Abacus.

LEVEL – 2

WORKBOOK 1 OF 2

PUBLISHED BY SAI SPEED MATH ACADEMY

USA

www.abacus-math.com

Published in the United States of America by SAI Speed Math Academy, 2014

The Library of Congress has cataloged this book under this catalog number:
Library of Congress Control Number: 2014907005

ISBN of this edition: 978-1-941589-04-5

Thanks to **Abiraaman Amarnath** for his valuable contribution towards the development of this book.

www.abacus-math.com
Edited by: WordPlay
www.wordplaynow.com
Front Cover Image: © [Yael Weiss] / Dollar Photo Club
Printed in the United States of America

Our Heartfelt Thanks to:

Our

Higher Self,

Family,

Teachers,

And Friends

For the support, guidance and confidence they gave us to…

…become one of the rare people who don't know how to quit. (~Robin Sharma)

KIND REQUEST

We believe knowledge is sacred.

We believe that knowledge has to be shared.

We could have monopolized our knowledge by franchising our work and creating wealth for ourselves. However, we choose to publish books so we can reach more parents and teachers who are interested in empowering their children with mind math at a very affordable cost and with the convenience of teaching at home.

Please help us know that we made the right decision by publishing books.

- ❖ We request that you please buy our books first hand to motivate us and show us your support.
- ❖ Please do not buy used books.
- ❖ We kindly ask you to refrain from copying this book in any form.
- ❖ Help us by introducing our books to your family and friends.

We are very grateful and truly believe that we are all connected through these books. We are very grateful to all the parents who have called in or emailed us to show their appreciation and support.

Thank you for trusting us and supporting our work.

With Best Regards,

SAI Speed Math Academy

Dear Parents and Teachers,

Thank you very much for buying this workbook. We are honored that you choose to use this workbook to help your child learn math and mind math using the Japanese abacus called the "Soroban". This is our humble effort to bring a much needed practice workbook to soroban enthusiasts around the world.

This book is the product of over six years of intense practice, research, and analysis of soroban. It has been perfected through learning, applying, and teaching the techniques to many students who have progressed and completed all six levels of our course successfully.

We are extremely grateful to all who have been involved in this extensive process and with the development of this book.

We know that with *effort, commitment* and *tenacity*, everyone can learn to work on soroban and succeed in mind math.

We wish all of you an enriching experience in learning to work on abacus and enjoying mind math excellence!

We are still learning and enjoying every minute of it!

INSTRUCTION BOOK FOR PARENTS/TEACHERS

Workbooks do not contain any instruction on what is taught within the lessons or how to use an abacus. All instructions are in the Instruction Book that is sold separately under the title:
    Abacus Mind Math Level – 2 Instruction Book – ISBN 978-1-941589-03-8

GOAL AFTER COMPLETION OF LEVEL 2 – WORKBOOKS 1 AND 2

On successful completion of the two workbooks students would be able to:

1. Add any two to three digit numbers that involve carry-over or regrouping problems.

HELPFUL SKILLS

- Must have mastered LEVEL – 1 concepts

PRACTICE WORKBOOKS FOR STUDENTS

This book is Abacus Mind Math Level - 2 Workbook 1 of 2. Continue working with Abacus Mind Math Level 2 – **Workbook 2 of 2** after finishing this workbook to complete LEVEL – 2 training.

Workbook 2 of 2 is **sold separately** and is available under the title:

Abacus Mind Math Level – 2 Workbook 2 of 2 – ISBN: 978-1-941589-05-2

WE WOULD LIKE TO HEAR FROM YOU!

Please visit our Facebook page at https://www.facebook.com/AbacusMindMath.
Contact us through http://www.abacus-math.com/contactus.php or email us at **info@abacus-math.com**

We Will Award Your Child a Certificate Upon Course Completion:

Once your child completes the test given at the back of the workbook – 2, please upload pictures of your child with completed test and marks scored on our Facebook page at **https://www.facebook.com/AbacusMindMath**, and at our email address: **info@abacus-math.com**

Provide us your email and we will email you a personalized certificate for your child. Please include your child's name as you would like for it to appear on the certificate.

LEARNING INSTITUTIONS AND HOME SCHOOLS

If you are from any public, charter or private school, and want to provide the opportunity of learning mind math using soroban to your students, please contact us. This book is a good teaching/learning aid for small groups or for one on one class. Books for larger classrooms are set up as 'Class work books' and 'Homework books'. These books will make the teaching and learning process a smooth, successful and empowering experience for teachers and students. We can work with you to provide the best learning experience for your students.

If you are from a home school group, please contact us if you need any help.

Contents

HOW TO USE THIS WORKBOOK 1

PARTS OF ABACUS...3

STUDENT'S SITTING POSITION 4

CLEARING OR SETTING ABACUS AT ZERO 4

FINGERING 5

ADDING AND SUBTRACTING.............................6

PLACE VALUE OF RODS 7

ORDER OF OPERATION......................................7

REVISION OF LEVEL 1 CONCEPTS 7

WEEK 1 – LESSON 1 – BIG FRIEND
COMBINATIONS 8

    LESSON 1 – ACTIVITY – 1.......................11

    LESSON 1 – ACTIVITY – 2.......................14

    LESSON 1 – ACTIVITY – 3.......................15

    LESSON 1 – PRACTICE WORK – REVISION OF
    LEVEL – 1 CONCEPTS 16

    LESSON 1 – MIND MATH PRACTICE WORK..19

    LESSON 1 – DICTATION 20

WEEK 2 – LESSON 2 – INTRODUCING + 9
CONCEPT 21

    LESSON 2 – PRACTICE WORK 21

    LESSON 2 – MIND MATH PRACTICE WORK..24

    LESSON 2 – DICTATION 25

    SKILL BUILDING 26

WEEK 3 – LESSON 3 – COMPLETING + 9 USING
SMALL FRIENDS FORMULA 28

    LESSON 3 – PRACTICE WORK 28

    LESSON 3 – MIND MATH PRACTICE WORK..31

    LESSON 3 – DICTATION 32

    SKILL BUILDING 33

WEEK 4 – LESSON 4 – INTRODUCING + 8
CONCEPT 35

    LESSON 4 – PRACTICE WORK 35

    LESSON 4 – MIND MATH PRACTICE WORK..38

    LESSON 4 – DICTATION 39

    SKILL BUILDING 40

WEEK 5 – LESSON 5 – COMPLETING + 8 USING
SMALL FRIENDS FORMULA 43

    LESSON 5 – PRACTICE WORK 43

    LESSON 5 – MIND MATH PRACTICE WORK..46

    LESSON 5 – DICTATION 47

    SKILL BUILDING 48

WEEK 6 – LESSON 6 – INTRODUCING + 7
CONCEPT 51

    LESSON 6 – PRACTICE WORK 51

    LESSON 6 – MIND MATH PRACTICE WORK..54

    LESSON 6 – DICTATION 55

    SKILL BUILDING 56

WEEK 7 – LESSON 7 – COMPLETING + 7 USING
SMALL FRIENDS FORMULA 58

    LESSON 7 – PRACTICE WORK 58

    LESSON 7 – MIND MATH PRACTICE WORK..61

LESSON 7 – DICTATION 62

SKILL BUILDING 63

WEEK 8 – SKILL BUILDING 66

WEEK 8 – PRACTICE WORK 66

WEEK 8 – MIND MATH PRACTICE WORK.....69

WEEK 8 – DICTATION 70

WEEK 9 – LESSON 8 – INTRODUCING + 6
CONCEPT 72

LESSON 8 – PRACTICE WORK 72

LESSON 8 – MIND MATH PRACTICE WORK..75

LESSON 8 – DICTATION 76

SKILL BUILDING 77

WEEK 10 – LESSON 9 – COMPLETING + 6 USING
SMALL FRIENDS FORMULA 79

LESSON 9 – PRACTICE WORK 79

LESSON 9 – MIND MATH PRACTICE WORK..82

LESSON 9 – DICTATION 83

SKILL BUILDING 84

ANSWER KEY 86

HOW TO USE THIS WORKBOOK

This workbook is for 10 weeks. Work in order given.

Each and every child is unique in his/her ability to learn. Sometimes a lesson might have to be repeated to get better understanding. You can erase the answers and redo the same lesson. On the other hand you may choose to move through the lessons quicker if child is an easy learner.

Each week's work is grouped together. Finish all the pages under each week before moving on to the next week's work. Work is divided for 5 days and you may choose to combine any number of days if you want to finish in shorter time. But, be very careful when you choose to do this, because children get overwhelmed easily when introduced to too many new concepts in a short time without having enough time to understand and practice.   Use your best judgment since you know your child's temperament and learning capabilities.

After finishing a DAY's work check the answer and redo the problems with the wrong answer.

Wish you all the best!

INTRODUCTION
Sit at a desk with a comfortable height.
Study the picture and learn the names of the different parts of the abacus.
Practice clearing your abacus a few times.

FINGERING
Correct fingering is very important so, practice moving earth beads and heaven beads using the correct fingers.

WEEKS 1 – Big friend combination facts are introduced. LEVEL – 1 concept practiced.

WEEKS 2 to 10 – Big friend formulas for +9, +8, +7, and +6 are introduced. Students will work with 2 digit and 3 digit numbers.

* Continue working with ABACUS MIND MATH LEVEL 2 – WORKBOOK 2 OF 2 after finishing this workbook to complete LEVEL – 2 training.

KEEPING TRACK

TIME: Make note of the time it takes your student to finish each day's work.

GOAL: As student progresses through the week they should be able to do their work in less time with more accuracy.

GRADES: Correct their work and calculate grade. Let your student color the stars next to each day's work. This will keep them engaged and encouraged.

HOW TO CALCULATE GRADE?

$$\frac{\text{Number of correct problems}}{\text{Total number of problems}} \times 100 = \text{Percentage scored}$$

GRADES

GRADE	PERCENTAGE		STAR COLOR
A+	96-100	EXTRAORDINARY	GOLD
A	91-95	EXCELLENT	
B+	86-90	AWESOME	SILVER
B	81-85	GOOD	
C	76-80	CONGRATULATIONS	BROWN
C+	70-75	CONGRATULATIONS	

PARTS OF ABACUS

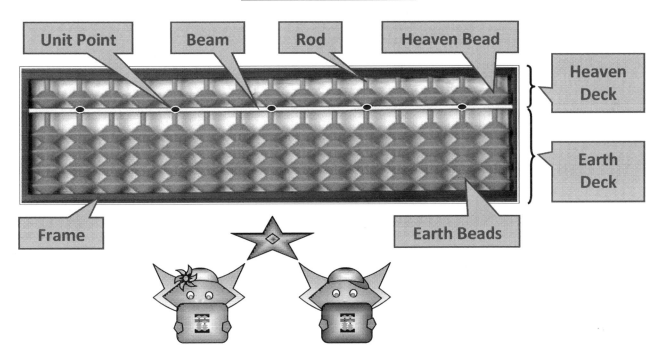

FRAME	Holds all the rods, beads and beam in place.
ROD	Sticks that hold the beads. Beads slide up or down on the rod.
BEADS	Represents numbers on the abacus. They slide on the rod and touch the beam or the frame. When beads touch the frame then your abacus is set at zero.
BEAM	The bar (usually white) that runs across all the rods and separates the Heaven and Earth beads. Only when beads touch the beam do they have value.
UNIT POINT	Can be used as decimal point. Can be used as comma that separates numbers by thousands. Example: $ 102,387,555 = One hundred and two million, three hundred eighty seven thousand, five hundred and fifty five dollars.
HEAVEN BEAD	There is one heaven bead above the beam on each rod. Each heaven bead is equal to "five".
EARTH BEADS	There are four earth beads below the beam on each rod. Each earth bead is equal to "one".

STUDENT'S SITTING POSITION

Sit at a table and place the abacus on the table with the heaven bead deck away from you. Please make sure that the table is not too high for the student.

CLEARING OR SETTING ABACUS AT ZERO

TRADITIONAL METHOD

STEP 1: Place the abacus on the table

STEP 2: Lift it with the bottom frame still touching the table. This will send all the earth beads to "zero" position

STEP 3: Gently place the abacus back on the table without moving the earth beads

STEP 4: Then place your finger between the heaven bead and the beam near the left hand side of the abacus

STEP 5: Drag your finger along the beam till to you reach the other side of the frame.

This will clear the heaven bead and send them to "zero" position

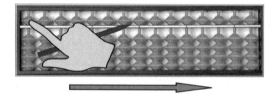

FUN METHOD: ZOOM AND CLEAR

STEP 1: Hold your thumb and pointer finger touching each other.

STEP 2: Place your fingers on the right side of the abacus beam with the beam in between the fingers like you are holding them very gently.

STEP 3: Now hold your abacus with the left hand so that the abacus does not move.

STEP 4: Now gently glide your fingers while still holding the beam, from the right side of the frame to the left side of the frame.

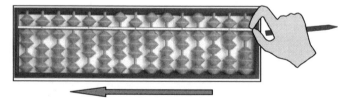

Clear your abacus every time you start a new calculation.

FINGERING

JOB OF THE THUMB (1):

A. Used to push the Earth Beads up to the beam, adding them to the game (ADD).

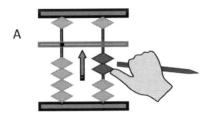

JOB OF THE POINTER FINGER (3):

1. Used to push the Earth Beads away from the beam, removing them from the game (MINUS).
2. Used to push the Heaven bead down to touch the beam, adding it to the game (ADD).
3. Used to push the Heaven bead away from the beam, removing it from the game (MINUS).

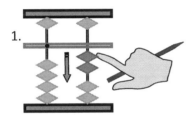 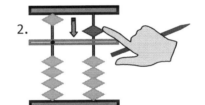 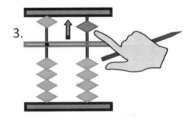

JOB OF THE OTHER THREE FINGERS:

Use your other three fingers to hold your pencil with the point facing down or away from you.

ADDING AND SUBTRACTING

ACTION FOR	ADDING	MINUS OR SUBTRACTING
EARTH BEADS	• When we say "adding" then it means we are moving the earth bead up to the beam with our thumb. • When the earth bead is touching the beam then it is "in the game" and is included in the reading.	• When we say "minus" then it means we are moving the earth bead away from the beam and making it touch the frame or other beads that are not in the game with your pointer finger. • When the earth bead touches the frame then it means that the bead is "out of the game" and is not read.
HEAVEN BEADS	• When we say "adding" it means we are moving the heaven bead with pointer finger to touch the beam. • When the heaven bead touches the beam it means that it is in the game and is included in the reading.	• When we say "minus" then it means we are moving the heaven bead with our pointer finger away from the beam to make it touch the frame. • When the heaven bead touches the frame then it means that the bead is "out of the game" and is not read.

PLACE VALUE OF RODS

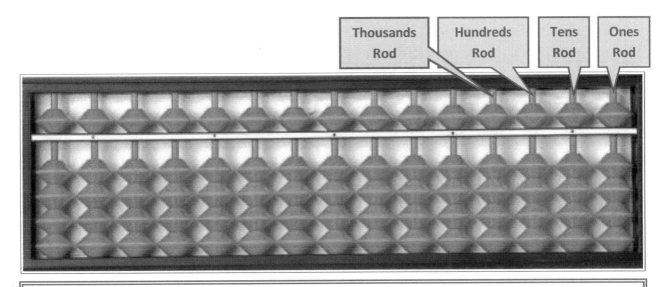

First rod from right is for the **ones place number**. All the ones place number will be set on this rod.

Second rod from right is for the **tens place number**. All the tens place number will be set on this rod.

Third rod from right is for the **hundreds place number**. All the hundreds place number will be set on this rod.

ORDER OF OPERATION

LEFT T/O RIGHT: When working with two digit numbers: always add or subtract the tens place number first and then work on the ones place number.

REVISION OF LEVEL 1 CONCEPTS

SMALL FRIEND FORMULAS

TO ADD	TO MINUS
$+1 = +5 - 4$	$-1 = -5 + 4$
$+2 = +5 - 3$	$-2 = -5 + 3$
$+3 = +5 - 2$	$-3 = -5 + 2$
$+4 = +5 - 1$	$-4 = -5 + 1$

WEEK 1 – LESSON 1 – BIG FRIEND COMBINATIONS

GOAL: For your child to know the **two numbers that add up to ten and hundred**.
There are five such set of combinations for 10 which are 9 & 1, 8 & 2, 7 & 3, 6 & 4, and 5 & 5. There are five such set of combinations for 100 which are 90 & 10, 80 & 20, 70 & 30, 60 & 40, and 50 & 50.

BIG FRIEND COMBINATION OF 10

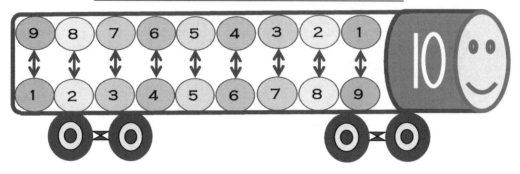

NUMBER SENTENCE FOR COMBINATIONS OF 10
Addition Facts

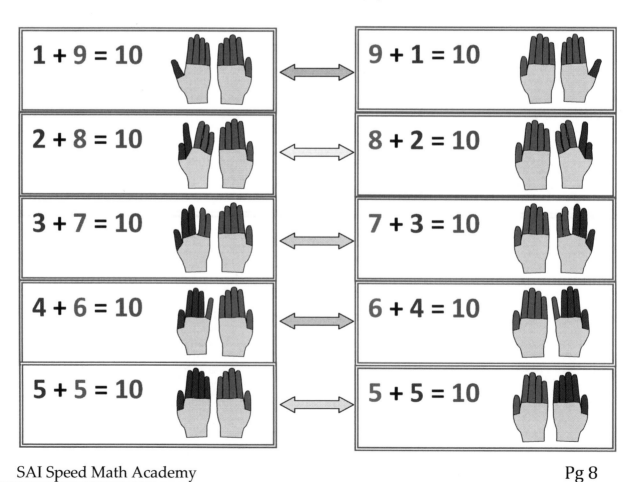

1 + 9 = 10	**9 + 1 = 10**
2 + 8 = 10	**8 + 2 = 10**
3 + 7 = 10	**7 + 3 = 10**
4 + 6 = 10	**6 + 4 = 10**
5 + 5 = 10	**5 + 5 = 10**

BIG FRIEND COMBINATION OF 100

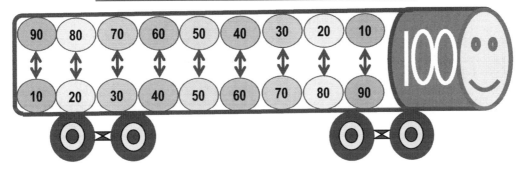

NUMBER SENTENCE FOR COMBINATIONS OF 100
Addition Facts

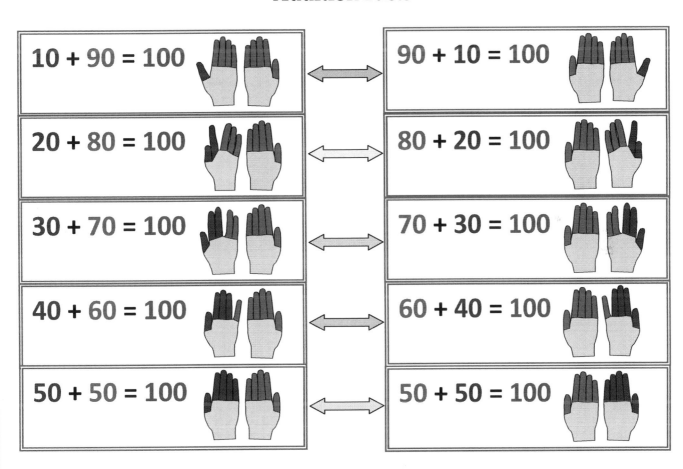

By using fingers, it is easy for children to memorize the fact family and also understand the big friend combination formulas. When using fingers to represent numbers adding up to 10, each finger is equal to 'one'. When using fingers to represent numbers adding up to 100, each finger is equal to 'ten'. Please do not worry that it would confuse your child because children will easily understand the concept. With practice, they will perfect their understanding.

BIG FRIEND FACTS OF 10

1 and 9 are big friends, because together they make 10.

2 and 8 are big friends, because together they make 10.

3 and 7 are big friends, because together they make 10.

4 and 6 are big friends, because together they make 10.

5 and 5 are big friends, because together they make 10.

BIG FRIEND COMBINATION FACTS FOR 100

10 and 90 are big friends of 100, because together they make 100.

20 and 80 are big friends of 100, because together they make 100.

30 and 70 are big friends of 100, because together they make 100.

40 and 60 are big friends of 100, because together they make 100.

50 and 50 are big friends of 100, because together they make 100.

POINTS TO REMEMBER

Make sure student understands the relation between big friend combination numbers. All the concepts introduced in LEVEL – 2 will be using these big friend relationship facts to attain the desired results of adding 9 to 1 by manipulating the beads in a certain order.

The big friends concepts introduced in this level are like walls of a building, thorough understanding of these facts is vital for their success with multiplication taught in higher levels. So, please make sure that students understand LEVEL – 2 concepts very well.

LESSON 1 – ACTIVITY – 1

DRAW A PICTURE (of anything) TO SHOW THE NUMBER SENTENCES

Example: $4 + 6 = 10$

DAY 1 - MONDAY

$9 + 1 = 10$ $8 + 2 = 10$

$+ \bigcirc = 10$

$7 + 3 = 10$ $6 + 4 = 10$

$5 + 5 = 10$ $4 + 6 = 10$

$3 + 7 = 10$ $2 + 8 = 10$

$1 + 9 = 10$

DAY 2 - TUESDAY

9 + 1 = 10   8 + 2 = 10

7 + 3 = 10   6 + 4 = 10

5 + 5 = 10   4 + 6 = 10

3 + 7 = 10   2 + 8 = 10

1 + 9 = 10

DAY 3 - WEDNESDAY

9 + 1 = 10   8 + 2 = 10

7 + 3 = 10   6 + 4 = 10

5 + 5 = 10

DAY 4 - THURSDAY

9 + 1 = 10   8 + 2 = 10

7 + 3 = 10   6 + 4 = 10

5 + 5 = 10   4 + 6 = 10

3 + 7 = 10   2 + 8 = 10

1 + 9 = 10

DAY 5 - FRIDAY

9 + 1 = 10   8 + 2 = 10

7 + 3 = 10   6 + 4 = 10

5 + 5 = 10

LESSON 1 – ACTIVITY – 2

Color the circle if the number sentence is true. Cross the circle if the number sentence is wrong.

Example: ● 9 + 1 = 10   ⊗ 2 + 7 = 10   ● 6 + 4 = 10

DAY 1
- ○ 7 + 3 = 10
- ○ 9 + 4 = 10
- ○ 8 + 2 = 10
- ○ 9 + 1 = 10
- ○ 5 + 4 = 10
- ○ 6 + 4 = 10
- ○ 5 + 5 = 10
- ○ 3 + 2 = 10
- ○ 1 + 9 = 10

DAY 2
- ○ 5 + 4 = 10
- ○ 8 + 2 = 10
- ○ 1 + 9 = 10
- ○ 3 + 2 = 10
- ○ 7 + 3 = 10
- ○ 5 + 5 = 10
- ○ 3 + 7 = 10
- ○ 5 + 3 = 10
- ○ 4 + 6 = 10

DAY 3
- ○ 5 + 3 = 10
- ○ 8 + 2 = 10
- ○ 4 + 1 = 10
- ○ 5 + 5 = 10
- ○ 7 + 3 = 10
- ○ 6 + 5 = 10
- ○ 9 + 1 = 10
- ○ 4 + 6 = 10
- ○ 3 + 8 = 10

DAY 4
- ○ 6 + 4 = 10
- ○ 9 + 3 = 10
- ○ 8 + 2 = 10
- ○ 1 + 9 = 10
- ○ 5 + 6 = 10
- ○ 2 + 9 = 10
- ○ 3 + 7 = 10
- ○ 5 + 5 = 10
- ○ 5 + 3 = 10

DAY 5
- ○ 4 + 3 = 10
- ○ 3 + 7 = 10
- ○ 5 + 5 = 10
- ○ 2 + 3 = 10
- ○ 8 + 2 = 10
- ○ 4 + 6 = 10
- ○ 2 + 3 = 10
- ○ 9 + 1 = 10
- ○ 3 + 6 = 10

DAY 6
- ○ 9 + 1 = 10
- ○ 5 + 4 = 10
- ○ 6 + 4 = 10
- ○ 5 + 5 = 10
- ○ 9 + 2 = 10
- ○ 2 + 8 = 10
- ○ 6 + 4 = 10
- ○ 7 + 3 = 10
- ○ 1 + 4 = 10

LESSON 1 – ACTIVITY – 3

Color the circle if the number sentence is true. Cross the circle if the number sentence is wrong.

Example: ● 90 + 10 = 100   ⊗ 20 + 70 = 100   ● 60 + 40 = 100

DAY 1
- ○ 80 + 20 = 100
- ○ 60 + 40 = 100
- ○ 70 + 20 = 100
- ○ 40 + 10 = 100
- ○ 50 + 40 = 100
- ○ 30 + 70 = 100
- ○ 10 + 90 = 100
- ○ 50 + 50 = 100
- ○ 10 + 40 = 100

DAY 2
- ○ 10 + 40 = 100
- ○ 40 + 20 = 100
- ○ 90 + 90 = 100
- ○ 70 + 30 = 100
- ○ 50 + 50 = 100
- ○ 80 + 20 = 100
- ○ 60 + 60 = 100
- ○ 90 + 10 = 100
- ○ 40 + 60 = 100

DAY 3
- ○ 70 + 30 = 100
- ○ 20 + 80 = 100
- ○ 30 + 20 = 100
- ○ 40 + 60 = 100
- ○ 50 + 50 = 100
- ○ 10 + 90 = 100
- ○ 40 + 10 = 100
- ○ 30 + 70 = 100
- ○ 10 + 80 = 100

DAY 4
- ○ 10 + 90 = 100
- ○ 50 + 50 = 100
- ○ 70 + 30 = 100
- ○ 90 + 10 = 100
- ○ 60 + 40 = 100
- ○ 80 + 20 = 100
- ○ 30 + 10 = 100
- ○ 20 + 30 = 100
- ○ 30 + 70 = 100

DAY 5
- ○ 70 + 30 = 100
- ○ 50 + 50 = 100
- ○ 10 + 80 = 100
- ○ 30 + 70 = 100
- ○ 20 + 80 = 100
- ○ 50 + 50 = 100
- ○ 40 + 40 = 100
- ○ 60 + 40 = 100
- ○ 80 + 20 = 100

DAY 6
- ○ 50 + 50 = 100
- ○ 40 + 60 = 100
- ○ 90 + 10 = 100
- ○ 70 + 30 = 100
- ○ 50 + 10 = 100
- ○ 60 + 40 = 100
- ○ 20 + 80 = 100
- ○ 20 + 30 = 100
- ○ 10 + 90 = 100

LESSON 1 – PRACTICE WORK – REVISION OF LEVEL – 1 CONCEPTS

Use Abacus

DAY 1 – MONDAY

TIME: _____min _____sec   Accuracy _____/16 ☆

1	2	3	4	5	6	7	8	
68	75	24	44	66	77	85	36	
- 44	- 44	31	31	- 43	21	- 34	12	
31	11	- 44	- 42	32	- 42	- 41	- 44	1:1
- 54	14	15	52	- 14	- 43	21	12	

1	2	3	4	5	6	7	8	
			13	98	22	656	234	
99	52	62	43	- 32	34	- 12	232	
- 41	- 21	24	- 12	- 21	- 33	- 313	- 23	1:2
- 31	34	- 31	44	- 13	42	68	134	
12	- 31	- 32	- 57	- 32	13	- 395	- 25	

DAY 2 – TUESDAY

TIME: _____min _____sec   Accuracy _____/16 ☆

1	2	3	4	5	6	7	8	
24	55	35	12	44	55	32	63	
30	- 10	- 24	34	31	- 20	25	31	
- 03	40	41	50	- 40	- 04	- 46	- 41	1:3
- 40	- 23	21	- 13	21	24	14	- 32	

1	2	3	4	5	6	7	8	
47	42	65	58	54	45	115	314	
11	12	- 14	- 44	21	31	141	31	
- 34	- 41	11	61	- 44	- 43	- 14	441	1:4
55	32	- 42	- 43	- 20	- 13	232	- 225	
- 43	21	15	27	65	68	125	136	

DAY 3 – WEDNESDAY

TIME: _____ min _____ sec   Accuracy _____ /16 ☆

1	2	3	4	5	6	7	8	
15	59	44	22	73	43	47	23	
- 01	- 33	12	32	- 31	21	- 34	31	
32	23	- 45	- 14	11	- 14	43	- 41	1:5
12	- 34	31	30	- 43	31	10	24	

1	2	3	4	5	6	7	8	
56	55	14	42	45	43	25	23	
- 14	- 11	11	32	- 22	21	- 12	32	
22	22	31	- 21	43	- 11	32	- 14	1:6
31	- 33	- 42	- 21	- 31	- 40	- 44	48	
- 52	22	51	53	- 31	32	18	- 55	

DAY 4 – THURSDAY

TIME: _____ min _____ sec   Accuracy _____ /16 ☆

1	2	3	4	5	6	7	8	
79	65	54	34	53	43	75	45	
- 34	- 41	22	21	- 41	33	- 41	13	
- 34	32	- 44	- 41	64	- 44	- 14	- 55	1:7
13	31	13	61	- 45	11	25	61	

1	2	3	4	5	6	7	8	
68	75	14	44	66	77	85	36	
- 44	- 44	31	31	- 43	21	- 34	12	
31	11	44	- 42	32	- 42	- 41	- 44	1:8
- 54	14	- 15	13	14	- 43	26	12	
72	33	- 41	12	- 57	61	21	52	

TIME: _____min _____sec   Accuracy _____/16 ☆

1	2	3	4	5	6	7	8
53	24	44	45	46	34	41	40
12	30	25	21	- 22	12	- 30	22
- 34	- 40	- 51	- 45	11	- 24	57	- 31
27	13	- 13	77	- 10	41	- 63	24

1	2	3	4	5	6	7	8
25	54	43	32	46	55	55	52
21	13	32	34	11	- 41	- 22	33
- 14	- 61	- 21	- 41	- 24	12	53	- 41
36	20	- 11	- 14	- 12	21	- 42	- 41
- 44	53	55	18	- 21	31	51	92

SKILL BUILDING EXERCISE

Draw beads to show numbers given.

115	295	401	260	639

Monday

227	905	610	397	803

Wednesday

LESSON 1 – MIND MATH PRACTICE WORK

DAY 1 – MONDAY

Accuracy _____/10 ☆

1	2	3	4	5	6	7	8	9	10
24	45	42	43	66	14	85	43	43	51
- 13	- 31	21	31	- 21	40	- 32	41	21	25
42	14	- 32	- 21	42	- 30	- 31	- 32	- 32	- 31
- 22	40	15	34	- 11	- 12	14	13	21	- 44

1:11

DAY 2 – TUESDAY

Accuracy _____/10 ☆

1	2	3	4	5	6	7	8	9	10
55	43	42	43	46	63	25	15	57	34
- 41	12	12	24	13	- 22	- 14	43	- 16	23
15	- 14	02	- 31	- 32	46	82	- 34	11	- 43
- 23	- 31	- 34	- 34	- 12	- 13	- 43	22	- 20	- 11

1:12

DAY 3 – WEDNESDAY

Accuracy _____/10 ☆

1	2	3	4	5	6	7	8	9	10
11	22	23	24	25	21	44	13	23	32
24	24	24	34	- 03	44	11	44	41	44
11	- 11	- 31	- 13	50	11	- 22	- 12	- 52	- 51
41	44	42	40	- 20	21	13	33	44	44

1:13

DAY 4 – THURSDAY

Accuracy _____/10

1	2	3	4	5	6	7	8	9	10
24	43	33	47	73	95	34	99	31	88
32	11	42	- 24	- 31	- 12	53	- 54	44	- 42
- 13	- 13	- 23	- 13	15	- 21	- 45	44	- 32	- 31
11	- 21	- 21	71	- 34	- 41	- 41	- 13	14	- 14

1:14

DAY 5 – FRIDAY

Accuracy _____/10

1	2	3	4	5	6	7	8	9	10
13	54	41	23	32	11	14	55	75	35
41	05	44	- 11	- 21	35	- 11	- 04	- 30	21
- 40	- 30	- 34	24	11	10	42	32	21	- 40
12	- 21	- 20	- 21	- 22	- 44	- 12	- 33	- 44	- 12

1:15

LESSON 1 – DICTATION

DICTATION: Dictation is when teacher or parent calls out a series of numbers and the child listens to the numbers and does the calculation in mind or on the abacus.

DO 6 PROBLEMS A DAY and write answers below.

1	2	3	4	5	6	7	8	9	10

11	12	13	14	15	16	17	18	19	20

21	22	23	24	25	26	27	28	29	30

WEEK 2 – LESSON 2 – INTRODUCING + 9 CONCEPT

LESSON 2 – PRACTICE WORK

+ 9 = +10 – 1

Use Abacus

DAY 1 – MONDAY

TIME: _____ min _____ sec   Accuracy _____/32

1	2	3	4	5	6	7	8	
11	22	13	14	17	23	65	35	
09	09	09	19	19	09	- 44	32	2:1
09	09	19	09	09	09	59	19	

1	2	3	4	5	6	7	8	
99	29	91	92	93	23	33	24	
90	90	94	92	92	31	11	11	
90	90	92	92	94	19	19	14	2:2
- 47	19	- 35	- 65	- 59	90	- 40	39	

1	2	3	4	5	6	7	8	
93	39	29	24	63	36	95	19	
94	29	49	09	- 42	90	- 91	09	
- 21	09	- 52	09	39	39	32	59	2:3
92	- 24	09	- 32	90	90	39	- 42	

1	2	3	4	5	6	7	8	
23	68	11	97	49	42	44	47	
93	09	09	- 64	30	29	99	92	
19	- 43	24	09	- 56	- 41	33	- 19	2:4
- 31	09	90	99	99	99	12	54	

DAY 2 – TUESDAY

TIME: _____min _____sec Accuracy _____/16

1	2	3	4	5	6	7	8	
22	23	34	06	07	17	20	44	
09	09	09	09	09	- 15	20	10	
91	09	90	90	90	22	20	21	2:5
- 11	90	25	90	19	99	99	91	

1	2	3	4	5	6	7	8	
14	39	64	29	14	75	29	43	
94	09	09	90	24	- 32	99	99	
09	- 26	- 23	90	09	99	99	- 22	2:6
19	95	19	- 09	- 47	11	- 25	31	

DAY 3 – WEDNESDAY

TIME: _____min _____sec Accuracy _____/16

1	2	3	4	5	6	7	8	
10	20	33	04	17	34	24	43	
90	09	90	19	09	99	91	11	
09	90	39	09	19	- 10	- 12	19	2:7
59	19	95	29	12	45	39	- 52	

1	2	3	4	5	6	7	8	
93	39	76	99	95	49	41	41	
90	49	- 32	- 31	- 12	99	99	18	
- 31	- 38	- 13	90	- 31	- 44	25	- 55	2:8
09	- 20	29	- 47	19	91	- 13	29	

DAY 4 – THURSDAY

TIME: _____min _____sec Accuracy _____/16

1	2	3	4	5	6	7	8
22	33	43	16	37	40	22	33
92	90	39	19	49	95	42	96
90	99	95	90	90	10	- 03	49
55	67	- 63	- 11	- 32	- 44	19	- 38

2:9

1	2	3	4	5	6	7	8
24	90	93	19	29	69	32	30
09	- 50	94	49	39	90	02	94
- 11	90	- 02	- 48	99	- 14	61	11
- 22	10	- 72	39	- 55	92	- 84	91

2:10

DAY 5 – FRIDAY

TIME: _____min _____sec Accuracy _____/16

1	2	3	4	5	6	7	8
08	19	66	77	84	84	32	25
09	49	09	90	91	11	55	21
90	90	90	90	- 34	- 53	11	19
90	- 16	- 11	- 14	19	19	- 97	90

2:11

1	2	3	4	5	6	7	8
25	23	22	29	49	64	36	54
- 01	09	92	09	19	91	- 22	01
99	- 22	99	91	- 35	- 35	30	- 12
- 22	29	45	- 04	99	58	19	99

2:12

LESSON 2 – MIND MATH PRACTICE WORK

DAY 1 – MONDAY

Accuracy _____/10 ☆

1	2	3	4	5	6	7	8	9	10	
39	34	19	29	12	41	24	59	21	55	
09	09	09	09	09	90	- 11	- 35	09	- 11	2:13
- 20	- 30	- 04	- 20	09	- 01	09	09	59	19	

DAY 2 – TUESDAY

Accuracy _____/10 ☆

1	2	3	4	5	6	7	8	9	10	
23	52	54	22	45	34	19	24	30	61	
09	30	- 01	04	- 24	53	- 09	02	90	90	2:14
- 01	- 60	09	90	09	- 45	09	09	60	- 41	

DAY 3 – WEDNESDAY

Accuracy _____/10 ☆

1	2	3	4	5	6	7	8	9	10	
75	99	42	19	99	19	11	44	35	29	
- 21	90	19	09	- 79	09	21	19	- 11	90	2:15
09	- 40	30	- 06	90	90	91	- 33	90	- 19	

DAY 4 – THURSDAY

Accuracy _____/10 ☆

1	2	3	4	5	6	7	8	9	10	
35	31	14	11	31	32	64	04	44	16	
90	29	90	90	29	90	90	61	19	90	2:16
- 11	09	90	09	- 10	50	01	90	- 50	09	

Accuracy _____/20 ☆

1	2	3	4	5	6	7	8	9	10	
24	24	34	44	34	49	28	41	34	75	
09	90	11	19	91	- 35	- 01	03	09	- 31	2:17
10	01	90	- 63	- 01	91	09	01	- 43	19	

© SAI Speed Math Academy, USA

1	2	3	4	5	6	7	8	9	10	
24	22	11	45	29	26	55	40	76	24	
39	12	51	01	90	40	- 10	03	- 54	90	2:18
- 51	90	90	90	- 18	99	90	99	19	90	

© SAI Speed Math Academy, USA

LESSON 2 – DICTATION

DICTATION: Dictation is when teacher or parent calls out a series of numbers and the child listens to the numbers and does the calculation in mind or on the abacus.

DO 6 PROBLEMS A DAY and write answers below.

Students: Try to calculate the dictated problems in mind.

Teachers: Dictate problems from mind math part of this week's homework.

1	2	3	4	5	6	7	8	9	10

11	12	13	14	15	16	17	18	19	20

21	22	23	24	25	26	27	28	29	30

SKILL BUILDING

Visualize the numbers on the beam in your mind and draw it to represent the numbers given.

483	217	936	507	329

Tuesday

354	680	708	248	193

Thursday

SHAPE PUZZLE

Find out what each shape is worth.

Suggestion: Take as many numbers of beans, blocks or coins as the right side of the equation shows and share them on the shapes to the left side of the equation.

 + = 12

 + = 06

 + + = 13

 = _____   = _____   = _____

DRAW A PICTURE OF YOUR HOME AND COLOR

WEEK 3 – LESSON 3 – COMPLETING + 9 USING SMALL FRIENDS FORMULA

+ 9 = +10 − 1(−5 +4)

LESSON 3 – PRACTICE WORK

Use Abacus

DAY 1 – MONDAY

TIME: _____min _____sec   Accuracy _____/32 ☆

1	2	3	4	5	6	7	8	
11	25	65	65	55	54	46	25	
49	09	90	90	90	91	09	19	3:1
90	09	09	90	19	19	99	19	

1	2	3	4	5	6	7	8	
29	24	63	14	39	64	29	14	
49	29	- 42	91	39	11	19	24	
- 26	29	39	09	- 26	- 30	19	19	3:2
90	- 32	19	- 13	91	19	- 46	- 57	

1	2	3	4	5	6	7	8	
93	39	76	99	95	95	99	93	
99	49	- 32	- 31	- 12	99	- 55	94	
- 91	- 38	- 13	90	- 31	- 50	99	- 02	3:3
59	90	19	90	19	09	19	- 72	

1	2	3	4	5	6	7	8	
25	34	24	16	49	23	68	15	
- 01	11	91	49	09	92	09	39	
99	09	39	99	- 33	19	- 43	99	3:4
- 22	94	90	- 31	29	19	19	99	

DAY 2 – TUESDAY

TIME: _____min _____sec   Accuracy _____/16

1	2	3	4	5	6	7	8	
93	39	19	29	97	49	43	49	
94	29	49	30	- 64	39	99	99	
- 21	09	- 48	90	39	- 33	14	- 44	3:5
92	- 24	90	- 45	19	09	99	49	

1	2	3	4	5	6	7	8	
36	95	49	42	55	47	211	323	
90	- 91	19	29	99	92	109	94	
39	32	19	- 41	33	- 19	49	- 314	3:6
09	19	- 42	99	12	90	- 243	129	

DAY 3 – WEDNESDAY

TIME: _____min _____sec   Accuracy _____/16

1	2	3	4	5	6	7	8	
21	19	69	46	99	19	134	339	
49	49	- 22	39	99	29	499	190	
29	- 15	09	09	- 55	09	- 13	- 24	3:7
- 99	92	90	- 94	09	90	- 620	09	

1	2	3	4	5	6	7	8	
29	51	83	54	11	44	152	94	
49	09	- 22	99	99	19	93	199	
- 38	90	99	09	69	29	09	199	3:8
19	90	99	- 51	- 59	- 52	- 254	- 451	

DAY 4 – THURSDAY

TIME: _____min _____sec   Accuracy _____/16

1	2	3	4	5	6	7	8
47	38	14	39	39	25	213	312
29	29	49	49	09	99	199	293
- 31	19	- 13	- 35	09	29	109	- 501
19	- 45	90	92	- 25	95	- 321	89

3:9

1	2	3	4	5	6	7	8
11	12	13	49	24	19	895	119
29	29	49	90	49	99	- 691	109
19	09	09	- 24	- 12	- 13	129	- 114
09	90	19	09	09	49	19	199

3:10

DAY 5 – FRIDAY

TIME: _____min _____sec   Accuracy _____/16

1	2	3	4	5	6	7	8
69	39	69	14	32	75	496	955
19	39	- 24	49	09	- 32	- 175	- 942
- 45	- 41	09	91	15	99	49	399
09	19	90	91	90	09	99	- 202

3:11

1	2	3	4	5	6	7	8
44	64	13	39	99	15	900	123
29	19	29	49	- 79	29	99	09
- 51	- 21	29	- 68	35	- 04	- 32	93
39	- 31	- 20	99	99	55	- 906	09

3:12

LESSON 3 – MIND MATH PRACTICE WORK

 Visualize

DAY 1 – MONDAY

Accuracy _____/10 ☆

1	2	3	4	5	6	7	8	9	10	
07	05	14	25	16	50	35	51	33	24	
09	09	09	09	09	90	- 11	90	09	01	3:13
09	- 11	- 23	20	09	- 40	19	- 30	09	09	

DAY 2 – TUESDAY

Accuracy _____/10 ☆

1	2	3	4	5	6	7	8	9	10	
04	61	45	11	15	99	18	56	70	55	
09	90	- 01	04	09	- 44	- 03	09	- 20	90	3:14
02	09	09	90	09	- 11	09	09	90	09	

DAY 3 – WEDNESDAY

Accuracy _____/10 ☆

1	2	3	4	5	6	7	8	9	10	
					39	34	19	29	12	
65	99	31	20	60	09	09	09	09	09	
- 21	- 44	19	90	90	- 40	- 30	- 04	- 20	09	3:15
09	90	40	- 10	90	09	- 01	- 20	90	- 30	

DAY 4 – THURSDAY

Accuracy _____/10 ☆

1	2	3	4	5	6	7	8	9	10	
					91	24	59	75	99	
65	41	55	15	26	90	- 11	- 35	- 21	90	
09	09	90	90	29	01	09	09	09	- 40	3:16
- 74	09	54	09	- 11	- 80	- 12	- 30	- 40	- 09	

1	2	3	4	5	6	7	8	9	10
15	80	22	25	50	13	15	66	40	56
09	90	99	19	90	12	09	- 22	11	99
30	- 30	09	11	10	19	15	33	90	- 55

3:17
© SAI Speed Math Academy, USA

1	2	3	4	5	6	7	8	9	10
23	52	54	22	45	34	19	24	42	59
09	30	- 01	03	- 24	53	- 09	02	09	90
- 01	- 60	09	09	09	- 45	40	09	90	- 04
09	09	10	- 04	09	90	90	09	10	09

3:18
© SAI Speed Math Academy, USA

LESSON 3 – DICTATION

DICTATION: Dictation is when teacher or parent calls out a series of numbers and the child listens to the numbers and does the calculation in mind or on the abacus.

DO 6 PROBLEMS A DAY and write answers below.
Students: Try to calculate the dictated problems in mind.
Teachers: Dictate problems from mind math part of this week's homework.

1	2	3	4	5	6	7	8	9	10

11	12	13	14	15	16	17	18	19	20

21	22	23	24	25	26	27	28	29	30

SKILL BUILDING

Visualize the numbers on the beam in your mind and draw it to represent the numbers given.

707	813	664	123	409	

Tuesday

348	951	266	570	931	

Thursday

SHAPES PUZZLE

Find out what each shape is worth.

Suggestion: Take as many numbers of beans, blocks or coins as the right side of the equation shows and share them on the shapes to the left side of the equation.

 + + + =

 + + + + = **35**

 − = **04**

 =_____   =_____   =_____

SAI Speed Math Academy

TALLY TIME

Woof the dog, Meow the cat and Baa the sheep were sitting in Ms. Owl's class. Each of them were asked to bring **9 pens, 19 erasers, 29 pencils and 93 crayons** to class.

Now they sat down to see how many pens, pencils, crayons and erasers they had in all.

Use your abacus to add and find the total

	PENS	ERASERS	PENCILS	CRAYONS
Woof				
Meow				
Baa				
TOTAL				

Total number of PENS _____   Total number of ERASERS _____

Total number of PENCILS _____   Total number of CRAYONS _____

Draw a picture of Ms. Owl's class

WEEK 4 – LESSON 4 – INTRODUCING + 8 CONCEPT

LESSON 4 – PRACTICE WORK

+ 8 = +10 – 2

Use Abacus

DAY 1 – MONDAY

TIME: _____min _____sec   Accuracy _____/32

1	2	3	4	5	6	7	8	
02	03	04	07	11	22	33	34	4:1
08	18	18	28	08	08	08	38	
80	08	18	80	08	08	18	08	

1	2	3	4	5	6	7	8	
18	22	38	28	87	77	78	99	4:2
18	08	29	08	98	89	81	89	
82	38	08	89	80	99	08	80	

1	2	3	4	5	6	7	8	
43	09	14	54	55	44	27	27	4:3
18	18	18	08	- 24	18	- 14	08	
29	18	38	- 30	48	- 12	28	19	
- 80	80	- 20	88	89	90	80	18	

1	2	3	4	5	6	7	8	
67	68	99	34	18	79	66	39	4:4
- 23	28	89	08	29	- 33	- 23	48	
88	- 44	- 33	38	18	09	80	- 34	
91	08	- 22	- 60	- 41	- 12	89	18	

DAY 2 – TUESDAY

TIME: _____ min _____ sec   Accuracy _____ /16 ☆

1	2	3	4	5	6	7	8
29	29	28	90	07	59	30	44
08	48	08	80	19	- 14	45	10
08	82	19	80	80	80	80	94
19	- 19	- 22	90	19	39	19	- 38

1	2	3	4	5	6	7	8
58	54	39	45	42	24	329	987
- 14	31	- 16	13	28	38	240	- 843
19	80	38	08	08	28	98	09
98	90	19	99	- 43	- 70	- 404	18

4:6

DAY 3 – WEDNESDAY

TIME: _____ min _____ sec   Accuracy _____ /16 ☆

1	2	3	4	5	6	7	8
55	44	12	12	28	52	35	25
- 21	88	49	28	18	- 20	- 11	84
08	- 12	08	38	81	48	08	18
19	80	98	- 14	- 14	18	08	08

4:7

1	2	3	4	5	6	7	8
95	94	77	28	84	33	307	999
- 41	88	- 33	38	- 12	38	89	- 801
18	09	98	- 44	81	- 21	- 284	188
18	98	18	89	- 50	90	48	- 172

4:8

© SAI Speed Math Academy, USA

DAY 4 – THURSDAY

TIME: _____ min _____ sec   Accuracy _____ /16 ☆

1	2	3	4	5	6	7	8
29	18	13	86	29	23	14	19
38	08	18	- 74	29	18	14	- 13
- 22	09	08	18	18	08	18	12
- 12	- 22	08	- 30	- 43	- 26	19	18

4:9

1	2	3	4	5	6	7	8
65	23	04	88	42	98	47	343
- 21	82	82	- 22	28	- 84	88	488
28	19	- 45	- 21	88	28	- 24	87
99	18	98	- 14	99	28	82	- 703

4:10

DAY 5 – FRIDAY

TIME: _____ min _____ sec   Accuracy _____ /16 ☆

1	2	3	4	5	6	7	8
49	18	45	86	39	55	74	59
18	28	19	89	89	99	84	- 13
08	39	08	89	18	08	08	32
80	- 22	08	98	- 43	- 31	- 22	188

4:11

1	2	3	4	5	6	7	8
56	44	44	77	42	78	57	104
- 12	89	82	- 33	28	- 34	18	88
82	29	33	88	28	28	19	87
12	08	- 18	14	98	82	- 90	- 137

4:12

LESSON 4 – MIND MATH PRACTICE WORK

Visualize

DAY 1 – MONDAY

Accuracy _____/10 ☆

1	2	3	4	5	6	7	8	9	10
14	13	18	54	14	20	40	40	44	66
08	08	09	08	08	80	80	80	18	- 33
08	08	08	- 22	18	80	90	30	- 12	08

4:13

DAY 2 – TUESDAY

Accuracy _____/10 ☆

1	2	3	4	5	6	7	8	9	10
34	50	54	70	25	08	45	16	44	04
08	90	08	80	80	80	80	- 02	19	18
03	80	08	- 50	09	08	- 25	08	- 22	18

4:14

DAY 3 – WEDNESDAY

Accuracy _____/10 ☆

1	2	3	4	5	6	7	8	9	10
				18	19	28	18	09	25
34	92	44	90	08	18	08	90	18	19
08	- 50	18	80	- 14	08	- 04	08	11	18
- 10	80	08	- 40	08	- 21	09	- 04	- 33	10

4:15

DAY 4 – THURSDAY

Accuracy _____/10 ☆

1	2	3	4	5	6	7	8	9	10
				54	43	89	25	55	39
12	42	14	40	08	35	- 76	09	90	80
12	80	14	42	- 30	- 08	08	08	80	- 14
08	80	08	08	08	80	09	80	09	09

4:16

Accuracy _____/20 ☆

1	2	3	4	5	6	7	8	9	10
05	70	24	34	75	49	25	70	59	75
19	80	18	19	80	80	19	- 30	- 19	19
08	90	09	08	09	- 19	22	80	80	- 64

4:17

© SAI Speed Math Academy, USA

1	2	3	4	5	6	7	8	9	10
12	14	11	22	85	30	17	11	31	02
09	08	21	30	80	80	08	80	80	09
08	08	- 30	08	- 01	90	09	80	12	03
- 05	19	08	90	- 04	08	- 04	08	08	08

4:18

© SAI Speed Math Academy, USA

LESSON 4 – DICTATION

DICTATION: Dictation is when teacher or parent calls out a series of numbers and the child listens to the numbers and does the calculation in mind or on the abacus.

DO 6 PROBLEMS A DAY and write answers below.

Students: Try to calculate the dictated problems in mind.

Teachers: Dictate problems from abacus math part of this week's homework.

1	2	3	4	5	6	7	8	9	10

11	12	13	14	15	16	17	18	19	20

21	22	23	24	25	26	27	28	29	30

SKILL BUILDING

Visualize the numbers on the beam in your mind and draw it to represent the numbers given.

| 746 | 832 | 650 | 481 | 948 |

Monday

| 202 | 674 | 812 | 501 | 376 |

Tuesday

| 554 | 270 | 490 | 327 | 385 |

Thursday

| 161 | 205 | 340 | 616 | 107 |

Friday

SHAPE PUZZLE

Find out what each shape is worth.

Suggestion: Take as many numbers of beans, blocks or coins as the right side of the equation shows and share them on the shapes to the left side of the equation.

 + + + = 16

 + + = 18

 − + = 12

 = _____   = _____   = _____

UNDERLINE ***UNSCRAMBLE:*** *Use the clues on the right side of the line to figure out the word scrambled on the left side of the line. Write your answer on the line. Make one sentence using each of these words.*

1. gemas _____ you play

2. yots _____ you play with

3. bcolks _____ you build with

4. nur _____ you do during play

5. nuf _____ you feel when you play

6. labl _____ you kick during a game

7. dsan _____ found at the beach

8. gwins _____ found on a play ground

9. sdlie _____ found on a play ground

10. ylap _____ you love to do this

Draw yourself in a flower garden with a butterfly on your nose with your best friends watching you! Don't forget to decorate the frame too.

WEEK 5 – LESSON 5 – COMPLETING + 8 USING SMALL FRIENDS FORMULA

+ 8 = +10 – 2(–5 +3)

LESSON 5 – PRACTICE WORK

Use Abacus

DAY 1 – MONDAY

TIME: _____ min _____ sec   Accuracy _____ /32

1	2	3	4	5	6	7	8	
15	47	29	34	37	63	43	56	5:1
08	08	18	80	18	89	22	88	
90	08	18	82	18	22	88	- 33	

1	2	3	4	5	6	7	8	
14	44	55	44	28	52	35	24	5:2
18	08	- 24	18	18	- 20	- 11	38	
38	80	48	- 12	18	48	08	83	
- 30	23	- 28	80	- 40	18	08	08	

1	2	3	4	5	6	7	8	
55	35	12	33	27	28	46	15	5:3
08	18	45	44	- 14	08	18	48	
- 12	80	80	- 22	38	08	08	18	
90	- 33	19	98	08	08	89	08	

1	2	3	4	5	6	7	8	
67	18	23	34	15	79	66	35	5:4
- 23	18	32	18	19	- 46	- 30	48	
08	19	90	38	18	13	18	- 81	
91	19	- 44	- 60	- 22	08	90	08	

DAY 2 – TUESDAY

TIME: _____min _____sec   Accuracy _____/16 ☆

1	2	3	4	5	6	7	8
43	09	39	45	58	54	63	44
18	18	- 16	13	- 14	31	92	12
29	18	38	08	38	80	18	98
- 80	08	19	18	91	90	- 63	80

5:5

1	2	3	4	5	6	7	8
95	94	99	28	84	44	307	999
- 11	81	- 88	38	- 12	38	89	- 801
- 34	- 22	94	08	81	- 41	- 284	188
18	83	48	08	- 50	14	48	- 182

5:6

DAY 3 – WEDNESDAY

TIME: _____min _____sec   Accuracy _____/16 ☆

1	2	3	4	5	6	7	8
54	77	42	78	57	105	65	152
82	- 33	28	- 34	18	39	89	82
- 33	88	28	28	18	08	- 41	39
88	14	98	82	- 90	- 131	139	- 43

5:7

1	2	3	4	5	6	7	8
45	86	19	55	74	59	67	155
18	88	29	99	84	- 13	- 21	198
08	91	- 13	08	08	32	88	- 122
98	89	18	- 31	- 11	18	99	- 101

5:8

DAY 4 – THURSDAY

TIME: _____min _____sec   Accuracy _____/16

1	2	3	4	5	6	7	8
19	39	47	11	55	91	59	229
98	80	08	18	89	84	- 18	480
80	28	18	18	11	81	28	89
- 94	- 44	92	18	98	- 24	- 09	- 554

5:9

1	2	3	4	5	6	7	8
21	18	39	54	19	36	88	389
89	28	08	98	18	08	81	288
28	- 14	28	83	18	- 12	18	- 552
18	09	- 45	- 34	- 21	90	81	28

5:10

DAY 5 – FRIDAY

TIME: _____min _____sec   Accuracy _____/16

1	2	3	4	5	6	7	8
26	86	25	23	14	49	67	102
28	- 74	29	18	31	- 13	- 42	193
08	34	18	18	08	18	39	- 140
80	08	- 40	89	- 11	92	- 41	98

5:11

1	2	3	4	5	6	7	8
04	55	15	58	47	115	65	442
48	90	28	90	22	38	189	282
90	08	08	28	- 15	81	- 41	- 304
08	80	80	- 34	98	- 203	138	48

5:12

LESSON 5 – MIND MATH PRACTICE WORK

Visualize

DAY 1 – MONDAY

Accuracy _____ /10 ☆

1	2	3	4	5	6	7	8	9	10
02	03	05	07	16	50	35	34	18	22
08	18	08	28	08	80	08	38	18	38
80	08	18	08	08	80	80	08	08	80

5:13

© SAI Speed Math Academy, USA

DAY 2 – TUESDAY

Accuracy _____ /10 ☆

1	2	3	4	5	6	7	8	9	10
37	26	55	27	78	56	47	19	28	60
29	08	90	89	- 24	90	08	48	40	80
08	22	08	08	80	08	08	80	80	80

5:14

© SAI Speed Math Academy, USA

DAY 3 – WEDNESDAY

Accuracy _____ /10 ☆

1	2	3	4	5	6	7	8	9	10
					28	34	15	17	95
65	35	27	16	19	08	08	08	18	- 40
- 21	08	28	38	40	- 04	80	30	08	80
08	08	08	80	80	08	- 22	80	- 21	19

5:15

© SAI Speed Math Academy, USA

DAY 4 – THURSDAY

Accuracy _____ /10 ☆

1	2	3	4	5	6	7	8	9	10
					18	14	06	65	70
24	45	61	61	25	08	12	18	- 31	90
21	09	80	90	18	18	18	11	08	80
08	80	14	80	- 43	- 44	22	19	10	- 40

5:16

© SAI Speed Math Academy, USA

Accuracy _____/20 ☆

1	2	3	4	5	6	7	8	9	10	
17	62	25	36	55	44	23	66	40	65	5:17
08	80	91	18	90	11	44	18	25	88	
18	- 30	08	- 11	18	80	80	- 84	80	- 53	

1	2	3	4	5	6	7	8	9	10	
53	11	54	13	45	43	50	23	55	35	5:18
08	14	08	12	40	10	90	22	- 41	18	
80	08	- 30	18	08	80	20	08	09	90	
10	12	08	- 33	- 53	25	80	90	08	- 23	

LESSON 5 – DICTATION

DICTATION: Dictation is when teacher or parent calls out a series of numbers and the child listens to the numbers and does the calculation in mind or on the abacus.

DO 6 PROBLEMS A DAY and write answers below.

Students: Try to calculate the dictated problems in mind.

Teachers: Dictate problems from mind math part of this week's homework.

1	2	3	4	5	6	7	8	9	10

11	12	13	14	15	16	17	18	19	20

21	22	23	24	25	26	27	28	29	30

SKILL BUILDING

Visualize the numbers on the beam in your mind and draw it to represent the numbers given.

145	399	507	519	625

Monday

613	247	350	282	198

Tuesday

239	438	568	121	377

Thursday

274	617	450	873	970

Friday

SHAPES PUZZLE

Find out what each shape is worth.

Suggestion: Take as many numbers of beans, blocks or coins as the right side of the equation shows and share them on the shapes to the left side of the equation.

WORD SEARCH

A	Z	L	D	Z	E	Z	G	E	C	K	O	I	Z
R	B	C	H	Z	F	F	G	R	O	G	E	C	S
G	G	O	O	S	E	R	A	I	D	L	I	O	N
O	E	B	A	C	D	B	E	A	V	E	R	E	O
O	S	T	R	I	C	H	R	L	R	B	F	Z	W
B	L	I	F	G	A	A	B	A	T	F	C	G	D
L	L	E	M	A	C	F	D	J	A	P	E	E	O
I	Y	R	D	O	F	H	A	R	F	J	B	G	G
E	N	O	O	Z	C	T	I	G	E	R	H	A	C
O	X	N	Z	E	I	G	F	W	E	A	S	E	L

GOOSE, BAT, RACOON, LION, GIRAFFE, APE, ZEBRA, CAMEL, BEAVER, LYNX, TIGER, GECKO, OSTRICH, WEASEL, CRAB, SNOW-DOG, OX

If the above animals have a party, what will be their favorite party food? Research their food habit and write a story of your favorite animals' birthday party.

WORD PROBLEM

Friends Anna, Bill, Gail, Joy and Mike decided to put up a lemonade stand. They each decided to bring lemons and sugar, to make the lemonade and cups to serve the lemonade.

1. Calculate how much supplies they had in total.

	LEMON	SUGAR in grams	CUPS
ANNA	45	126	55
BILL	19	328	98
GAIL	88	90	113
JOY	33	121	280
MIKE	08	189	108
TOTAL			

They sold a cup of lemonade for 8 cents. Fill in the table below and help them find out how much they made selling 10 cups of lemonade. (Hint: Skip count by eight)

1 cup	2 cups	3 cups	4 cups	5 cups	6 cups	7 cups	8 cups	9 cups	10 cups
8 cents									

They had sold 100 cups of lemonade by the end of the day. Now, fill in the table below to see how much they made selling 100 cups of lemonade. (Hint: You will know how much they made for 10 cups of lemonade from the above table.)

10 cups	20 cups	30 cups	40 cups	50 cups	60 cups	70 cups	80 cups	90 cups	100 cups

Total money they earned selling 100 cups of lemonade = _____ cents.

If 100 cents = 1 dollar.

Find out how many dollars they made in total by filling in the table below.

100 cents	200 cents	300 cents	400 cents	500 cents	600 cents	700 cents	800 cents
1 dollar							

Total money they raised selling 100 cups of lemonade = _____ dollars.

WEEK 6 – LESSON 6 – INTRODUCING + 7 CONCEPT

LESSON 6 – PRACTICE WORK

+ 7 = +10 − 3

Use Abacus

DAY 1 – MONDAY

TIME: _____min _____sec   Accuracy _____/32 ☆

1	2	3	4	5	6	7	8	
03	04	08	08	19	33	38	34	6:1
07	17	17	37	17	07	07	47	
79	75	71	70	70	70	71	70	

1	2	3	4	5	6	7	8	
37	27	78	88	87	89	29	55	6:2
12	08	97	77	71	79	70	98	
37	79	89	98	07	07	70	07	

1	2	3	4	5	6	7	8	
36	91	24	42	18	47	47	29	6:3
08	71	08	08	17	78	- 13	27	
17	28	07	07	19	72	27	- 14	
- 20	70	27	09	27	78	- 30	73	

1	2	3	4	5	6	7	8	
44	21	42	29	36	394	191	134	6:4
70	27	74	27	- 12	270	074	171	
17	17	33	21	37	107	- 31	173	
70	- 24	17	- 44	- 41	- 730	077	17	

DAY 2 – TUESDAY

TIME: _____ min _____ sec   Accuracy _____ /16 ☆

1	2	3	4	5	6	7	8	
				49	38	33	37	
79	28	15	94	77	37	77	78	6:5
17	07	79	74	89	- 21	98	- 01	
72	70	74	97	- 11	07	77	17	

1	2	3	4	5	6	7	8	
82	34	97	23	18	19	34	184	
77	31	- 73	37	07	27	174	177	6:6
- 11	29	67	17	18	08	27	- 230	
17	- 73	97	- 64	19	17	79	70	

DAY 3 – WEDNESDAY

TIME: _____ min _____ sec   Accuracy _____ /16 ☆

1	2	3	4	5	6	7	8	
65	54	22	33	48	21	34	28	
18	18	47	27	49	78	27	37	6:7
70	- 11	07	- 30	- 55	- 55	23	- 11	
87	- 41	- 53	70	74	47	71	17	

1	2	3	4	5	6	7	8	
88	43	43	47	99	18	142	394	
77	77	47	09	- 30	17	177	74	6:8
08	- 10	- 30	08	17	70	198	17	
09	37	19	17	72	49	- 106	- 341	

DAY 4 – THURSDAY

1	2	3	4	5	6	7	8
23	66	44	24	94	89	41	88
17	28	34	73	88	- 77	47	07
32	- 70	07	- 57	- 20	87	- 74	71
18	87	78	75	- 41	- 77	18	92

6:9

1	2	3	4	5	6	7	8
69	24	29	32	24	34	143	138
17	07	38	47	18	47	78	278
70	- 10	09	- 35	49	74	87	- 302
19	55	- 53	17	04	- 33	27	47

6:10

DAY 5 – FRIDAY

1	2	3	4	5	6	7	8
44	43	21	29	54	33	33	41
17	25	07	07	07	77	47	47
21	07	17	- 02	- 20	48	04	- 23
70	- 52	- 44	23	39	90	07	- 31

6:11

1	2	3	4	5	6	7	8
99	35	21	40	28	434	324	149
- 56	43	17	77	17	174	372	87
11	17	28	70	19	17	- 453	- 102
87	91	- 31	- 37	08	- 302	17	77

6:12

LESSON 6 – MIND MATH PRACTICE WORK

DAY 1 – MONDAY   Accuracy _____/10 ☆

1	2	3	4	5	6	7	8	9	10	
09	18	17	14	19	30	40	90	34	43	
07	07	- 03	17	17	70	70	70	07	17	6:13
- 03	08	07	- 31	- 23	02	40	- 30	70	- 30	

DAY 2 – TUESDAY   Accuracy _____/10 ☆

1	2	3	4	5	6	7	8	9	10	
24	08	44	40	20	60	45	29	45	04	
07	07	10	70	70	80	19	17	40	37	6:14
08	- 15	07	- 10	70	70	07	- 33	70	70	

DAY 3 – WEDNESDAY   Accuracy _____/10 ☆

1	2	3	4	5	6	7	8	9	10	
				34	59	35	22	14	95	
29	80	24	40	07	- 17	- 21	77	47	70	
07	- 40	37	74	07	04	19	- 80	- 30	- 21	6:15
- 33	70	- 40	07	19	- 15	07	07	70	70	

DAY 4 – THURSDAY   Accuracy _____/10 ☆

1	2	3	4	5	6	7	8	9	10	
				26	14	09	13	14	44	
56	49	24	50	72	17	37	77	27	27	
- 12	70	17	90	- 81	17	70	- 80	70	03	6:16
17	- 18	70	70	- 07	- 08	- 03	55	19	07	

Accuracy _____/20 ☆

1	2	3	4	5	6	7	8	9	10	
03	40	09	29	55	67	45	75	83	65	6:17
17	74	17	17	- 41	- 33	19	- 31	- 50	80	
80	07	33	70	17	70	07	70	77	09	

1	2	3	4	5	6	7	8	9	10	
68	34	88	79	95	48	39	44	40	14	6:18
27	07	- 07	07	- 70	09	47	73	70	74	
71	18	09	- 70	48	- 24	70	80	43	- 48	
- 33	37	72	53	07	70	- 13	- 22	17	70	

LESSON 6 – DICTATION

DICTATION: Dictation is when teacher or parent calls out a series of numbers and the child listens to the numbers and does the calculation in mind or on the abacus.

DO 6 PROBLEMS A DAY and write answers below.

Students: Try to calculate the dictated problems in mind.

Teachers: Dictate problems from abacus math part of this week's homework.

1	2	3	4	5	6	7	8	9	10

11	12	13	14	15	16	17	18	19	20

21	22	23	24	25	26	27	28	29	30

SKILL BUILDING

Visualize the numbers on the beam in your mind and draw it to represent the numbers given.

| 269 | 107 | 574 | 932 | 448 |

Monday

| 687 | 987 | 014 | 209 | 418 |

Tuesday

| 640 | 774 | 945 | 523 | 480 |

Thursday

| 304 | 430 | 366 | 700 | 491 |

Friday

SUDOKU

		2	
	4		
		3	
	1		

3			1
	4		
	3		
2			4

Fill in with numbers from 1 to 4. Make sure numbers do not repeat within each column, row or block

4		1	
	1		
		2	
1			3

2			3
		2	
	1		
4			1

WORD BANK

Think of words that end with 'it', like in 'sit' or 'at', like in 'cat' and write them on the line given. Use a dictionary to find more words and their meaning. Make a sentence using each of the words.

_____Sit_____   _____   _____   _____

_____   _____   _____   _____

_____   _____   _____   _____

_____   _____   _____   _____

_____   _____   _____   _____

WEEK 7 – LESSON 7 – COMPLETING + 7 USING SMALL FRIENDS FORMULA

+ 7 = +10 − 3(−5 +2)

LESSON 7 – PRACTICE WORK

Use Abacus

DAY 1 – MONDAY

TIME: _____ min _____ sec   Accuracy _____ /32

1	2	3	4	5	6	7	8
15	48	66	49	65	28	45	91
07	07	97	07	73	39	07	74
37	89	09	70	07	28	73	- 33

7:1

1	2	3	4	5	6	7	8
24	42	15	47	47	27	36	34
08	08	17	78	- 13	27	17	31
07	07	17	40	27	- 14	- 10	27
27	07	28	78	08	28	17	- 71

7:2

1	2	3	4	5	6	7	8
65	54	26	15	48	21	31	27
19	18	27	17	39	78	27	37
70	- 20	19	37	- 13	- 73	18	- 11
70	73	73	70	71	47	07	17

7:3

1	2	3	4	5	6	7	8
43	47	99	33	54	89	48	88
47	09	- 30	27	88	- 77	17	07
- 30	07	17	15	33	87	70	77
19	17	72	77	77	- 77	18	97

7:4

DAY 2 – TUESDAY

TIME: _____min _____sec   Accuracy _____/16

1	2	3	4	5	6	7	8
36	19	97	25	41	18	45	55
07	17	- 73	37	34	27	27	97
17	28	67	14	77	77	18	98
- 20	07	97	17	- 32	33	91	70

7:5

1	2	3	4	5	6	7	8
44	25	12	29	36	394	141	134
07	27	34	27	17	270	074	171
74	73	07	21	97	170	37	173
29	- 14	17	- 44	80	- 732	- 130	- 277

7:6

DAY 3 – WEDNESDAY

TIME: _____min _____sec   Accuracy _____/16

1	2	3	4	5	6	7	8
21	29	55	53	33	35	15	19
06	07	07	77	47	17	37	38
17	- 02	70	48	80	73	85	07
- 44	23	39	- 35	70	31	17	17

7:7

1	2	3	4	5	6	7	8
99	35	21	46	21	434	324	449
- 78	43	17	77	25	173	374	287
55	17	28	33	07	47	- 263	- 305
78	91	- 31	- 14	72	- 314	17	70

7:8

DAY 4 – THURSDAY

TIME: _____ min _____ sec   Accuracy _____/16   ☆

1	2	3	4	5	6	7	8
57	11	58	40	35	35	50	45
- 13	13	- 17	27	27	29	37	31
77	27	28	17	14	80	79	- 22
29	70	- 39	- 54	78	07	- 33	74

7:9 © SAI Speed Math Academy, USA

1	2	3	4	5	6	7	8
49	38	57	37	15	540	388	489
77	37	77	78	37	77	70	170
89	- 40	21	51	75	37	- 312	277
37	17	97	- 43	- 27	- 414	07	- 514

7:10 © SAI Speed Math Academy, USA

DAY 5 – FRIDAY

TIME: _____ min _____ sec   Accuracy _____/16   ☆

1	2	3	4	5	6	7	8
19	96	74	39	24	45	95	42
27	- 33	71	77	21	- 31	- 70	23
27	19	07	21	18	78	27	70
75	09	70	17	07	- 70	78	- 33

7:11 © SAI Speed Math Academy, USA

1	2	3	4	5	6	7	8
64	44	13	55	413	798	132	558
- 52	13	37	07	77	- 477	273	- 103
28	97	75	07	- 260	14	48	70
47	98	29	- 49	75	17	- 312	27

7:12 © SAI Speed Math Academy, USA

LESSON 7 – MIND MATH PRACTICE WORK

Visualize

DAY 1 – MONDAY

Accuracy _____/10 ☆

1	2	3	4	5	6	7	8	9	10	
03	05	08	36	59	32	33	44	79	27	
07	07	17	07	07	04	27	27	70	07	7:13
79	33	07	70	70	07	70	70	07	77	

© SAI Speed Math Academy, USA

DAY 2 – TUESDAY

Accuracy _____/10 ☆

1	2	3	4	5	6	7	8	9	10	
37	26	55	66	85	35	26	55	15	64	
12	07	70	79	70	17	18	78	27	70	7:14
37	22	19	07	- 33	70	77	- 33	74	18	

© SAI Speed Math Academy, USA

DAY 3 – WEDNESDAY

Accuracy _____/10 ☆

1	2	3	4	5	6	7	8	9	10	
					42	24	13	15	54	
16	26	17	44	60	07	37	27	17	04	
07	07	47	17	70	40	70	17	22	- 33	7:15
70	70	70	- 61	- 30	07	- 11	70	70	17	

© SAI Speed Math Academy, USA

DAY 4 – THURSDAY

Accuracy _____/10 ☆

1	2	3	4	5	6	7	8	9	10	
					18	65	44	75	47	
29	36	71	66	25	07	- 11	17	- 31	08	
27	17	70	70	19	07	17	70	08	90	7:16
07	- 41	20	08	70	43	- 31	05	70	07	

© SAI Speed Math Academy, USA

1	2	3	4	5	6	7	8	9	10
47	55	36	22	55	45	75	86	49	66
08	70	17	44	90	07	70	70	07	80
07	- 14	- 43	77	08	90	17	08	80	17

7:17

1	2	3	4	5	6	7	8	9	10
37	26	44	40	42	34	99	25	88	49
17	33	41	30	79	53	- 72	28	07	38
14	80	70	85	08	- 17	30	90	- 50	- 32
- 05	19	07	17	- 17	70	70	- 43	17	77

7:18

LESSON 7 – DICTATION

DICTATION: Dictation is when teacher or parent calls out a series of numbers and the child listens to the numbers and does the calculation in mind or on the abacus.

DO 6 PROBLEMS A DAY and write answers below.

Students: Try to calculate the dictated problems in mind.

Teachers: Dictate problems from mind math part of this week's homework.

1	2	3	4	5	6	7	8	9	10

11	12	13	14	15	16	17	18	19	20

21	22	23	24	25	26	27	28	29	30

SKILL BUILDING

Visualize the numbers on the beam in your mind and draw it to represent the numbers given.

863	129	342	623	715

Monday

307	495	830	224	837

Tuesday

034	629	142	840	965

Thursday

240	900	806	769	171

Friday

SEPARATE SHAPES

Example: Separate the smiley with 3 straight lines and give them their own space.
Lines can touch or cross each other.

Draw 4 straight lines to separate the stars and give them their own space.

Use 4 straws to figure out the place of your lines before you draw them on paper.

JUMPING RACE

A group of Kangaroo friends had a jumping race. Each was proud of how far they could jump and they decided to see who jumped the farthest in 30 seconds.

Kangaroo Jo leaped 9 feet every time she jumped. She was able to jump 11 times in 30 seconds.
Kangaroo Ben leaped 8 feet every time he jumped. He was able to jump 12 times in 30 seconds.
Kangaroo Su leaped 7 feet every time she jumped. She was able to jump 14 times in 30 seconds.

Find out how many total feet each kangaroo jumped in 30 seconds.
(Hint: add 9 eleven times to find out how far kangaroo Jo jumped. Add 8 twelve times to find out how far kangaroo Ben jumped and add 7 fourteen times to find out how far kangaroo Su jumped.)

	Kangaroo Jo 9 feet per jump	Kangaroo Ben 8 feet per jump	Kangaroo Su 7 feet per jump
1st Jump			
2nd Jump			
3rd Jump			
4th Jump			
5th Jump			
6th Jump			
7th Jump			
8th Jump			
9th Jump			
10th Jump			
11th Jump			
12th Jump			
13th Jump			
14th Jump			
TOTAL FEET JUMPED			

 Winner of the race is _____

WEEK 8 – SKILL BUILDING

WEEK 8 – PRACTICE WORK

DAY 1 – MONDAY

TIME: _____ min _____ sec   Accuracy _____ /16

1	2	3	4	5	6	7	8	
19	35	15	57	11	33	234	333	
47	28	77	97	74	27	22	72	
09	24	- 60	11	07	82	99	- 101	8:1
17	- 70	42	87	- 90	94	78	- 102	

1	2	3	4	5	6	7	8	
13	17	44	15	41	22	443	124	
67	67	47	27	19	44	112	87	
05	- 30	- 50	39	84	08	- 320	55	8:2
- 42	14	19	- 41	23	79	57	- 132	

DAY 2 – TUESDAY

TIME: _____ min _____ sec   Accuracy _____ /16

1	2	3	4	5	6	7	8	
77	45	37	71	55	36	44	141	
- 23	08	17	28	- 11	27	17	177	
12	70	92	- 44	07	18	84	78	8:3
27	- 23	- 43	98	70	09	17	- 123	

1	2	3	4	5	6	7	8	
14	35	33	24	47	50	715	466	
78	19	72	18	17	07	- 400	- 312	
- 61	32	48	25	- 20	79	39	77	8:4
77	07	- 32	17	31	- 33	- 254	26	

DAY 3 – WEDNESDAY

TIME: _____ min _____ sec   Accuracy _____ /16

1	2	3	4	5	6	7	8
57	13	46	46	35	35	155	315
- 13	13	17	27	17	27	198	377
02	09	- 21	73	13	08	177	- 640
07	18	18	- 44	18	- 70	- 410	79

8:5

1	2	3	4	5	6	7	8
32	32	43	46	34	45	657	144
25	23	13	07	47	37	- 504	88
18	29	98	07	07	- 42	97	73
17	- 84	- 14	- 40	- 83	09	- 210	48

8:6

DAY 4 – THURSDAY

TIME: _____ min _____ sec   Accuracy _____ /16

1	2	3	4	5	6	7	8
43	24	69	25	29	41	666	285
34	73	- 47	27	38	47	- 140	87
07	- 57	39	- 10	09	- 33	128	- 120
- 40	77	17	08	- 53	97	- 321	079

8:7

1	2	3	4	5	6	7	8
26	35	48	21	36	27	97	394
47	27	49	78	27	37	- 73	270
07	- 30	- 85	- 73	98	- 11	67	170
- 50	73	74	47	70	17	97	- 732

8:8

1	2	3	4	5	6	7	8	
24	46	15	56	47	27	22	34	
08	08	17	87	- 13	27	17	31	8:9
07	07	17	14	27	72	- 11	27	
27	70	28	70	08	28	17	- 71	

© SAI Speed Math Academy, USA

1	2	3	4	5	6	7	8	
43	47	95	15	94	88	41	88	
47	09	- 30	17	88	- 44	47	07	8:10
- 30	07	70	37	- 20	11	- 74	77	
19	17	19	80	- 41	97	18	93	

© SAI Speed Math Academy, USA

WORD SEARCH

Words that have similar meaning to 'GOOD' are listed in the box on the right. Use a **dictionary** (learn to use a real dictionary) and find the meaning to the listed words and write down a sentence describing yourself using these words. Then try to find the words hiding here.

```
K  O  D  E  H  S  I  L  P  M  O  C  C  A
R  W  E  Q  L  U  F  L  L  I  K  S  Z  E
I  O  C  U  D  W  N  E  D  N  J  N  D  L
E  N  N  I  H  U  I  X  G  C  J  N  E  B
N  D  E  L  H  R  V  C  O  R  I  B  C  A
I  E  I  E  L  B  A  E  P  E  I  B  E  P
F  R  R  H  Z  M  C  L  L  D  J  B  N  A
S  F  E  J  T  M  O  L  R  I  K  X  T  C
S  U  P  E  R  B  P  E  W  B  K  R  N  C
N  L  X  Y  Y  G  P  N  W  L  Q  Q  A  A
A  D  E  T  I  F  G  T  R  E  P  X  E  A
```

Fine
Able
Gifted
Expert
Decent
Superb
Skillful
Capable
Excellent
Incredible
Wonderful
Experienced
Accomplished

WEEK 8 – MIND MATH PRACTICE WORK

Visualize

DAY 1 – MONDAY

Accuracy _____ /10 ☆

1	2	3	4	5	6	7	8	9	10
34	59	35	22	16	95	19	29	39	17
07	- 37	27	77	17	- 31	27	07	77	37
07	04	19	- 84	- 10	70	19	70	13	84
19	17	07	07	57	08	07	07	09	- 37

8:11

DAY 2 – TUESDAY

Accuracy _____ /10 ☆

1	2	3	4	5	6	7	8	9	10
59	56	65	44	26	17	09	13	35	44
- 17	09	07	72	72	17	37	77	37	27
39	- 40	83	37	- 81	17	70	- 80	17	05
08	37	17	- 33	- 17	- 40	18	55	- 43	07

8:12

DAY 3 – WEDNESDAY

Accuracy _____ /10 ☆

1	2	3	4	5	6	7	8	9	10
68	35	88	79	55	48	39	44	120	14
27	17	- 07	07	78	09	47	73	90	74
- 70	18	09	- 70	23	17	- 40	07	87	- 17
17	07	72	07	- 34	18	- 03	- 22	- 95	- 71

8:13

DAY 4 – THURSDAY

Accuracy _____ /10 ☆

1	2	3	4	5	6	7	8	9	10
45	25	13	19	54	18	65	49	65	42
07	37	27	17	04	19	17	17	- 31	08
70	04	17	01	- 37	17	- 30	17	08	05
- 11	- 45	07	20	- 21	43	08	- 53	70	19

8:14

DAY 5 – FRIDAY   Accuracy _____/20 ☆

1	2	3	4	5	6	7	8	9	10
39	26	44	46	42	34	99	24	88	49
- 17	33	41	37	79	53	- 44	21	- 47	38
14	- 17	- 72	- 41	08	- 17	07	10	06	09
- 03	09	07	08	- 17	70	89	07	27	- 55

8:15 © SAI Speed Math Academy, USA

1	2	3	4	5	6	7	8	9	10
87	26	16	32	65	41	25	28	55	42
07	07	27	24	70	24	09	07	- 12	37
- 50	17	07	37	90	- 30	17	80	43	- 42
18	- 20	- 30	- 50	07	17	- 11	09	07	28

8:16 © SAI Speed Math Academy, USA

WEEK 8 – DICTATION

DICTATION: Dictation is when teacher or parent calls out a series of numbers and the child listens to the numbers and does the calculation in mind or on the abacus.

DO 6 PROBLEMS A DAY and write answers below.
Students: Try to calculate the dictated problems in mind.
Teachers: Dictate problems from abacus math part of this week's homework.

1	2	3	4	5	6	7	8	9	10

11	12	13	14	15	16	17	18	19	20

21	22	23	24	25	26	27	28	29	30

SEPARATE SHAPES

Draw 3 straight lines to separate the shapes and give them their own space.

Use 3 straws to figure out the place of your lines before you draw them on paper.

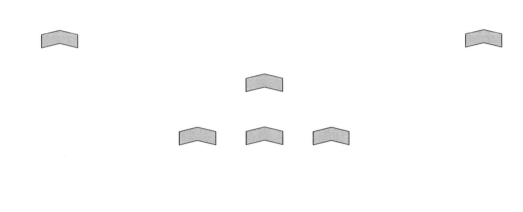

WORD BANK

Think of words that end with 'ip', like in 'zip' or 'an', like in 'tan' and write them on the line given. Use a dictionary to find more words and their meaning. Make a sentence using each of the words.

_____zip_____   _____   _____   _____

_____   _____   _____   _____

_____   _____   _____   _____

_____   _____   _____   _____

_____   _____   _____   _____

WEEK 9 – LESSON 8 – INTRODUCING + 6 CONCEPT

LESSON 8 – PRACTICE WORK

+ 6 = +10 – 4

Use Abacus

DAY 1 – MONDAY

TIME: _____ min _____ sec   Accuracy _____ /32

1	2	3	4	5	6	7	8
03	04	09	04	81	34	34	34
06	16	16	36	09	25	06	46
19	65	61	60	60	06	61	85

9:1

© SAI Speed Math Academy, USA

1	2	3	4	5	6	7	8
29	24	37	27	44	99	86	49
16	16	62	62	96	66	11	66
72	60	66	96	66	77	67	48

9:2

© SAI Speed Math Academy, USA

1	2	3	4	5	6	7	8
44	39	32	19	56	14	51	29
67	46	64	16	- 12	46	84	46
86	07	60	17	26	16	84	78
- 67	- 52	- 16	- 40	86	- 34	26	- 43

9:3

© SAI Speed Math Academy, USA

1	2	3	4	5	6	7	8
17	23	55	59	34	33	384	335
37	24	99	- 46	26	62	206	361
06	- 16	06	29	35	69	62	- 204
80	- 31	19	68	68	16	- 411	165

9:4

© SAI Speed Math Academy, USA

DAY 2 – TUESDAY

TIME: _____min _____sec   Accuracy _____/16 ☆

1	2	3	4	5	6	7	8
49	24	66	75	58	44	66	46
16	48	- 14	- 61	97	04	- 55	62
90	18	89	34	39	11	98	17
18	60	64	60	66	86	56	09

9:5 © SAI Speed Math Academy, USA

1	2	3	4	5	6	7	8
55	75	55	44	17	415	575	134
- 34	74	77	16	19	79	- 231	145
98	16	67	16	30	- 351	96	86
16	- 41	69	18	- 22	164	- 400	- 251

9:6 © SAI Speed Math Academy, USA

DAY 3 – WEDNESDAY

TIME: _____min _____sec   Accuracy _____/16 ☆

1	2	3	4	5	6	7	8
44	48	49	44	33	32	34	59
47	11	16	66	22	26	26	- 15
60	16	27	86	09	09	15	61
- 41	- 14	60	67	16	87	- 44	18

9:7 © SAI Speed Math Academy, USA

1	2	3	4	5	6	7	8
66	58	15	42	84	36	455	456
- 44	11	18	44	06	38	- 112	- 204
22	16	09	78	65	70	066	90
16	- 42	65	26	- 14	46	- 409	63

9:8 © SAI Speed Math Academy, USA

DAY 4 – THURSDAY

TIME: _____ min _____ sec   Accuracy _____ /16

1	2	3	4	5	6	7	8	
44	43	13	27	77	85	24	85	9:9
66	67	46	- 06	- 31	- 61	46	- 62	
78	86	16	68	11	74	06	47	
- 46	68	08	06	- 22	69	08	- 30	

1	2	3	4	5	6	7	8	
14	49	19	43	39	13	535	545	9:10
66	46	26	27	60	47	24	- 104	
- 30	- 60	11	- 40	- 56	14	- 415	160	
18	39	11	25	48	16	16	- 400	
70	15	09	97	69	- 80	74	49	

DAY 5 – FRIDAY

TIME: _____ min _____ sec   Accuracy _____ /16

1	2	3	4	5	6	7	8	
19	88	71	55	85	35	67	29	9:11
66	- 16	85	- 11	09	18	- 43	36	
- 54	- 71	32	16	66	37	16	19	
19	89	07	- 20	- 20	60	60	08	

1	2	3	4	5	6	7	8	
13	14	21	13	44	43	245	241	9:12
26	46	46	47	16	26	462	366	
26	18	- 24	16	14	28	- 300	68	
- 41	- 44	48	18	16	- 45	047	- 653	
22	11	60	96	- 50	- 12	- 412	34	

LESSON 8 – MIND MATH PRACTICE WORK

Visualize

DAY 1 – MONDAY

Accuracy _____/10 ☆

1	2	3	4	5	6	7	8	9	10	
24	13	09	44	04	90	45	05	44	66	
06	27	16	16	06	65	60	39	16	- 22	9:13
- 30	60	08	- 40	90	- 41	09	60	70	66	

DAY 2 – TUESDAY

Accuracy _____/10 ☆

1	2	3	4	5	6	7	8	9	10	
34	54	84	70	19	95	45	16	44	19	
26	90	06	70	16	60	17	- 02	96	16	9:14
- 10	- 44	60	60	- 31	08	- 40	16	60	19	

DAY 3 – WEDNESDAY

Accuracy _____/10 ☆

1	2	3	4	5	6	7	8	9	10	
				12	04	59	19	42	84	
55	66	77	88	60	06	06	06	17	70	
- 41	- 32	- 34	- 54	16	17	08	74	16	06	9:15
16	06	67	86	07	- 24	71	- 55	- 54	- 40	

DAY 4 – THURSDAY

Accuracy _____/10 ☆

1	2	3	4	5	6	7	8	9	10	
				99	24	65	45	45	26	
14	39	99	45	- 60	16	- 32	60	09	63	
45	36	66	61	06	07	06	09	16	- 55	9:16
06	- 51	09	08	- 41	- 46	- 09	56	70	46	

© SAI Speed Math Academy, USA

Accuracy _____/20 ☆

1	2	3	4	5	6	7	8	9	10
57	54	39	52	95	61	38	104	97	59
- 26	36	26	26	60	26	61	40	- 16	06
64	- 60	80	- 64	- 10	- 73	60	66	- 40	- 20
- 01	- 30	60	26	- 42	06	- 06	- 10	60	60

9:17 © SAI Speed Math Academy, USA

1	2	3	4	5	6	7	8	9	10
33	52	54	31	99	64	89	49	32	09
46	36	24	60	60	06	- 46	16	62	06
- 61	- 44	- 36	60	- 44	24	20	- 11	60	09
- 16	60	69	- 41	08	61	- 60	- 44	16	08

9:18 © SAI Speed Math Academy, USA

LESSON 8 – DICTATION

DICTATION: Dictation is when teacher or parent calls out a series of numbers and the child listens to the numbers and does the calculation in mind or on the abacus.

DO 6 PROBLEMS A DAY and write answers below.
Students: Try to calculate the dictated problems in mind.
Teachers: Dictate problems from abacus math part of this week's homework.

1	2	3	4	5	6	7	8	9	10

11	12	13	14	15	16	17	18	19	20

21	22	23	24	25	26	27	28	29	30

SKILL BUILDING

Visualize the numbers on the beam in your mind and draw it to represent the numbers given.

| 207 | 199 | 614 | 461 | 737 |

Monday

| 916 | 870 | 669 | 572 | 439 |

Tuesday

| 465 | 345 | 069 | 838 | 911 |

Thursday

| 590 | 702 | 320 | 049 | 144 |

Friday

SUDOKU

Fill in with the 4 different shapes. Make sure shapes do not repeat within each column, row or block

WORD BANK

Think of words that end with 'ad', like in 'fad' or 'in' like in 'Train' and write them on the line given. Use a dictionary to find more words and their meaning. Make a sentence using each of the words.

Fad _____ _____ _____ _____

_____ _____ _____ _____

_____ _____ _____ _____

_____ _____ _____ _____

_____ _____ _____ _____

WEEK 10 – LESSON 9 – COMPLETING + 6 USING SMALL FRIENDS FORMULA

+ 6 = +10 – 4(–5 +1) LESSON 9 – PRACTICE WORK

Use Abacus

DAY 1 – MONDAY

TIME: _____ min _____ sec   Accuracy _____/32

1	2	3	4	5	6	7	8	
19	02	11	32	34	34	69	24	10:1
06	36	06	06	06	46	16	16	
61	06	06	06	61	60	62	60	

1	2	3	4	5	6	7	8	
32	19	56	15	51	24	16	23	10:2
64	17	- 12	46	04	21	37	24	
60	16	26	60	64	26	65	- 16	
67	- 30	64	44	36	64	16	- 31	

1	2	3	4	5	6	7	8	
55	59	34	33	66	75	58	44	10:3
06	16	26	22	- 14	- 61	66	04	
06	61	16	61	87	34	39	16	
- 43	- 26	06	16	- 16	06	- 40	- 23	

1	2	3	4	5	6	7	8	
55	75	55	49	17	75	47	46	10:4
- 34	62	66	16	16	68	06	62	
96	16	67	76	32	13	62	17	
68	66	- 54	14	89	- 44	38	06	

DAY 2 – TUESDAY

TIME: _____ min _____ sec   Accuracy _____ /16

1	2	3	4	5	6	7	8	
55	39	44	48	66	58	39	66	
76	46	47	47	- 44	16	16	86	
86	07	- 30	66	38	- 30	97	13	10:5
- 14	- 52	64	- 40	60	06	- 11	- 41	

1	2	3	4	5	6	7	8	
49	45	33	32	43	35	487	434	
- 12	66	24	26	16	16	- 342	144	
27	45	96	06	- 22	75	169	- 431	10:6
64	- 12	- 13	07	56	- 24	36	06	

DAY 3 – WEDNESDAY

TIME: _____ min _____ sec   Accuracy _____ /16

1	2	3	4	5	6	7	8	
44	43	13	27	77	85	75	137	
11	67	22	16	- 31	- 61	79	16	
78	86	16	12	16	74	11	13	10:7
44	86	65	96	- 22	- 58	66	- 42	

1	2	3	4	5	6	7	8	
15	42	25	85	19	88	411	415	
17	44	46	- 42	66	- 14	66	76	
19	- 13	06	17	- 34	71	- 232	- 341	10:8
64	60	17	60	94	06	46	- 140	

DAY 4 – THURSDAY

TIME: _____ min _____ sec   Accuracy _____ /16   ☆

1	2	3	4	5	6	7	8
54	23	15	53	44	15	13	19
16	64	36	63	06	64	54	46
17	08	14	36	- 20	16	- 41	- 21
92	62	18	14	45	- 70	26	06
16	07	60	87	69	27	14	- 30

10:9 © SAI Speed Math Academy, USA

1	2	3	4	5	6	7	8
18	42	58	45	42	545	576	455
46	26	06	66	26	- 104	- 261	- 112
19	08	21	45	- 31	- 220	36	011
70	16	68	27	16	35	15	194
45	- 92	- 43	- 41	- 53	96	87	16

10:10 © SAI Speed Math Academy, USA

DAY 5 – FRIDAY

TIME: _____ min _____ sec   Accuracy _____ /16   ☆

1	2	3	4	5	6	7	8
49	08	56	55	38	99	19	17
76	76	17	76	16	66	16	36
60	- 61	64	19	11	- 45	20	17
70	08	- 13	60	89	26	- 11	85
- 14	39	29	41	96	68	44	- 24

10:11 © SAI Speed Math Academy, USA

1	2	3	4	5	6	7	8
14	26	49	64	444	593	155	535
16	68	26	65	161	- 160	169	17
16	66	- 31	29	- 502	75	41	- 210
49	27	26	- 44	62	- 301	87	11
- 15	66	- 40	- 14	86	46	- 242	- 230

10:12 © SAI Speed Math Academy, USA

LESSON 9 – MIND MATH PRACTICE WORK

Visualize

DAY 1 – MONDAY

Accuracy _____/10 ☆

1	2	3	4	5	6	7	8	9	10	
04	14	18	34	15	54	65	43	65	55	
06	16	06	21	16	90	70	23	60	76	10:13
49	65	44	06	70	06	06	60	16	- 31	

© SAI Speed Math Academy, USA

DAY 2 – TUESDAY

Accuracy _____/10 ☆

1	2	3	4	5	6	7	8	9	10	
37	27	44	46	87	49	27	75	52	24	
62	16	96	16	- 23	06	30	60	75	30	10:14
60	60	40	70	60	- 14	66	19	16	84	

© SAI Speed Math Academy, USA

DAY 3 – WEDNESDAY

Accuracy _____/10 ☆

1	2	3	4	5	6	7	8	9	10	
					52	06	48	19	42	
28	25	37	50	70	60	16	06	06	13	
16	06	40	65	60	44	28	- 40	74	80	10:15
06	70	06	- 13	- 10	- 12	- 10	90	- 55	06	

© SAI Speed Math Academy, USA

DAY 4 – THURSDAY

Accuracy _____/10 ☆

1	2	3	4	5	6	7	8	9	10	
					84	95	24	65	75	
44	16	65	55	35	70	60	16	- 32	60	
14	21	60	90	16	06	06	07	23	08	10:16
06	16	08	07	90	- 60	- 41	- 46	- 14	55	

© SAI Speed Math Academy, USA

Accuracy _____/20 ☆

1	2	3	4	5	6	7	8	9	10	
41	26	33	52	54	34	99	68	89	49	10:17
06	63	44	65	14	16	- 32	06	- 44	30	© SAI Speed Math Academy, USA
11	- 18	16	90	06	15	80	- 60	19	- 16	
11	- 61	80	- 04	70	- 21	07	- 14	60	80	

1	2	3	4	5	6	7	8	9	10	
57	54	55	52	85	51	38	55	97	111	10:18
- 23	36	26	26	60	26	61	06	- 16	40	© SAI Speed Math Academy, USA
46	- 60	- 60	60	- 10	70	- 80	- 20	- 40	90	
- 80	- 30	89	17	- 24	16	- 06	03	60	- 140	

LESSON 9 – DICTATION

DICTATION: Dictation is when teacher or parent calls out a series of numbers and the child listens to the numbers and does the calculation in mind or on the abacus.

DO 6 PROBLEMS A DAY and write answers below.
Students: Try to calculate the dictated problems in mind.
Teachers: Dictate problems from mind math part of this week's homework.

1	2	3	4	5	6	7	8	9	10

11	12	13	14	15	16	17	18	19	20

21	22	23	24	25	26	27	28	29	30

SKILL BUILDING

Visualize the numbers on the beam in your mind and draw it to represent the numbers given.

| 401 | 600 | 615 | 535 | 166 |

Monday

| 187 | 284 | 417 | 820 | 055 |

Tuesday

| 197 | 924 | 999 | 773 | 317 |

Thursday

| 435 | 313 | 571 | 799 | 061 |

Friday

DRAW 4 STRAIGHT LINES TO GIVE EACH HEART THEIR OWN SPACE

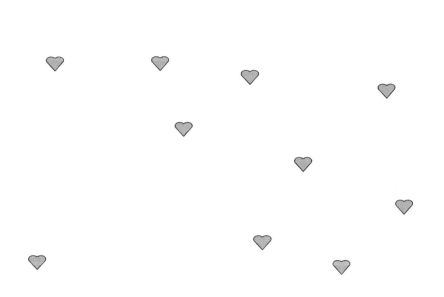

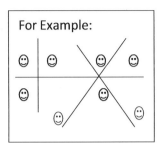

For Example:

UNSCRAMBLE: THINK GARDEN!

AELF	FOUND ON A PLANT, PRODUCES FOOD
ISOL	MOM TELLS YOU NOT TO GET THIS ON YOUR DRESS
ALTNP	NEED TO STOP CUTTING THIS TO SAVE EARTH
TORO	A TREE'S LEG
RIUTF	HEALTHY SNACK
LOFREW	HONEY BEE FINDS FOOD IN HERE
ORMW	FOUND IN GARDEN SOIL
ARKB	DOGS LIKE TO DO THIS BUT A TREE NEEDS IT
ACHBNR	CAN CALL THIS AS A HAND OF A TREE
SAGSR	WHEN YOU FALL ON THIS IT LOVES TO STAIN YOUR DRESS

ANSWER KEY

WEEK 1 – LESSON 1

1	2	3	4	5	6	7	8	
01	56	26	85	41	13	31	16	1:1

1	2	3	4	5	6	7	8	
39	34	23	31	00	78	04	552	1:2

1	2	3	4	5	6	7	8	
11	62	73	83	56	55	25	21	1:3

1	2	3	4	5	6	7	8	
36	66	35	59	76	88	599	697	1:4

1	2	3	4	5	6	7	8	
58	15	42	70	10	81	66	37	1:5

1	2	3	4	5	6	7	8	
43	55	65	85	04	45	19	34	1:6

1	2	3	4	5	6	7	8	
24	87	45	75	31	43	45	64	1:7

1	2	3	4	5	6	7	8	
73	89	33	58	12	74	57	68	1:8

1	2	3	4	5	6	7	8	
58	27	05	98	25	63	05	55	1:9

1	2	3	4	5	6	7	8	
24	79	98	29	00	78	95	95	1:10

LESSON 1 – MIND MATH PRACTICE WORK

1	2	3	4	5	6	7	8	9	10	
31	68	46	87	76	12	36	65	53	01	1:11

1	2	3	4	5	6	7	8	9	10	
06	10	22	02	15	74	50	46	32	03	1:12

1	2	3	4	5	6	7	8	9	10	
87	79	58	85	52	97	46	78	56	69	1:13

1	2	3	4	5	6	7	8	9	10	
54	20	31	81	23	21	01	76	57	01	1:14

1	2	3	4	5	6	7	8	9	10	
26	08	31	15	00	12	33	50	22	04	1:15

WEEK 2 – LESSON 2

1	2	3	4	5	6	7	8	
29	40	41	42	45	41	80	86	2:1

1	2	3	4	5	6	7	8	
232	228	242	211	220	163	23	88	2:2

1	2	3	4	5	6	7	8	
258	53	35	10	150	255	75	45	2:3

1	2	3	4	5	6	7	8	
104	43	134	141	122	129	188	174	2:4

1	2	3	4	5	6	7	8	
111	131	158	195	125	123	159	166	2:5

1	2	3	4	5	6	7	8	
136	117	69	200	00	153	202	151	2:6

1	2	3	4	5	6	7	8	
168	138	257	61	57	168	142	21	2:7

1	2	3	4	5	6	7	8	
161	30	60	111	71	195	152	33	2:8

1	2	3	4	5	6	7	8	
259	289	114	114	144	101	80	140	2:9

1	2	3	4	5	6	7	8	
00	140	113	59	112	237	11	226	2:10

1	2	3	4	5	6	7	8	
197	142	154	243	160	61	01	155	2:11

1	2	3	4	5	6	7	8	
101	39	258	125	132	178	63	142	2:12

SHAPES PUZZLE

△ = 06   ■ = 04

⬤ = 03

LESSON 2 – MIND MATH PRACTICE WORK

1	2	3	4	5	6	7	8	9	10	
28	13	24	18	30	130	22	33	89	63	2:13

1	2	3	4	5	6	7	8	9	10	
31	22	62	116	30	42	19	35	180	110	2:14

1	2	3	4	5	6	7	8	9	10	
63	149	91	22	110	118	123	30	114	100	2:15

1	2	3	4	5	6	7	8	9	10	
114	69	194	110	50	172	155	155	13	115	2:16

1	2	3	4	5	6	7	8	9	10	
43	115	135	00	124	105	36	45	00	63	2:17

1	2	3	4	5	6	7	8	9	10	
12	124	152	136	101	165	135	142	41	204	2:18

WEEK 3 – LESSON 3

1	2	3	4	5	6	7	8	
150	43	164	245	164	164	154	63	3:1

1	2	3	4	5	6	7	8	
142	50	79	101	143	64	21	00	3:2

1	2	3	4	5	6	7	8	
160	140	50	248	71	153	162	113	3:3

1	2	3	4	5	6	7	8	
101	148	244	133	54	153	53	252	3:4

1	2	3	4	5	6	7	8	
258	53	110	104	91	64	255	153	3:5

1	2	3	4	5	6	7	8	
174	55	45	129	199	210	126	232	3:6

1	2	3	4	5	6	7	8	
00	145	146	00	152	147	000	514	3:7

1	2	3	4	5	6	7	8	
59	240	259	111	120	40	00	41	3:8

1	2	3	4	5	6	7	8	
64	41	140	145	32	248	200	193	3:9

1	2	3	4	5	6	7	8	
68	140	90	124	70	154	352	313	3:10

1	2	3	4	5	6	7	8	
52	56	144	245	146	151	469	210	3:11

1	2	3	4	5	6	7	8	
61	31	51	119	154	95	61	234	3:12

LESSON 3 – MIND MATH PRACTICE WORK

1	2	3	4	5	6	7	8	9	10	
25	03	00	54	34	100	43	111	51	34	3:13

1	2	3	4	5	6	7	8	9	10	
15	160	53	105	33	44	24	74	140	154	3:14

1	2	3	4	5	6	7	8	9	10	
53	145	90	100	240	17	12	04	108	00	3:15

1	2	3	4	5	6	7	8	9	10	
00	59	199	114	44	102	10	03	23	140	3:16

1	2	3	4	5	6	7	8	9	10	
54	140	130	55	150	44	39	77	141	100	3:17

1	2	3	4	5	6	7	8	9	10	
40	31	72	30	39	132	140	44	151	154	3:18

SHAPES PUZZLE

☺ = 03   ◉ = 07

⊘ = 12

TALLY TIME

Total number of PENS	__	27
Total number of ERASERS	__	57
Total number of PENCILS	__	87
Total number of CRAYONS	__	279

WEEK 4 – LESSON 4 – INTRODUCING + 8 CONCEPT

1	2	3	4	5	6	7	8	
90	29	40	115	27	38	59	80	4:1

1	2	3	4	5	6	7	8	
118	68	75	125	265	265	167	268	4:2

1	2	3	4	5	6	7	8	
10	125	50	120	168	140	121	72	4:3

1	2	3	4	5	6	7	8	
223	60	133	20	24	43	212	71	4:4

1	2	3	4	5	6	7	8	
64	140	33	340	125	164	174	110	4:5

1	2	3	4	5	6	7	8	
161	255	80	165	35	20	263	171	4:6

1	2	3	4	5	6	7	8	
61	200	167	64	113	98	40	135	4:7

1	2	3	4	5	6	7	8	
90	289	160	111	103	140	160	214	4:8

1	2	3	4	5	6	7	8	
33	13	47	00	33	23	65	36	4:9

1	2	3	4	5	6	7	8	
171	142	139	31	257	70	193	215	4:10

1	2	3	4	5	6	7	8	
155	63	80	362	103	131	144	266	4:11

1	2	3	4	5	6	7	8	
138	170	141	146	196	154	04	142	4:12

LESSON 4 – MIND MATH PRACTICE WORK

1	2	3	4	5	6	7	8	9	10	
30	29	35	40	40	180	210	150	50	41	4:13

1	2	3	4	5	6	7	8	9	10	
45	220	70	100	114	96	100	22	41	40	4:14

1	2	3	4	5	6	7	8	9	10	
32	122	70	130	20	24	41	112	05	72	4:15

1	2	3	4	5	6	7	8	9	10	
32	202	36	90	40	150	30	122	234	114	4:16

1	2	3	4	5	6	7	8	9	10	
32	240	51	61	164	110	66	120	120	130	4:17

1	2	3	4	5	6	7	8	9	10	
24	49	10	150	160	208	30	179	131	22	4:18

SHAPES PUZZLE

 = 04   ♥ = 07

⌒ = 09

UNSCRAMBLE

1.	games
2.	toys
3.	blocks
4.	run
5.	fun
6.	ball
7.	sand
8.	swing
9.	slide
10.	play

WEEK 5 – LESSON 5

1	2	3	4	5	6	7	8	
113	63	65	196	73	174	153	111	5:1

1	2	3	4	5	6	7	8	
40	155	51	130	24	98	40	153	5:2

1	2	3	4	5	6	7	8	
141	100	156	153	59	52	161	89	5:3

1	2	3	4	5	6	7	8	
143	74	101	30	30	54	144	10	5:4

1	2	3	4	5	6	7	8	
10	53	80	84	173	255	110	234	5:5

1	2	3	4	5	6	7	8	
68	236	153	82	103	55	160	204	5:6

1	2	3	4	5	6	7	8	
191	146	196	154	03	21	252	230	5:7

1	2	3	4	5	6	7	8	
169	354	53	131	155	96	233	130	5:8

1	2	3	4	5	6	7	8	
103	103	165	65	253	232	60	244	5:9

1	2	3	4	5	6	7	8	
156	41	30	201	34	122	268	153	5:10

1	2	3	4	5	6	7	8	
142	54	32	148	42	146	23	253	5:11

1	2	3	4	5	6	7	8	
150	233	131	142	152	31	351	468	5:12

LESSON 5 – MIND MATH PRACTICE WORK

1	2	3	4	5	6	7	8	9	10	
90	29	31	43	32	210	123	80	44	140	5:13

1	2	3	4	5	6	7	8	9	10	
74	56	153	124	134	154	63	147	148	220	5:14

1	2	3	4	5	6	7	8	9	10	
52	51	63	134	139	40	100	133	22	154	5:15

1	2	3	4	5	6	7	8	9	10	
53	134	155	231	00	00	66	54	52	200	5:16

1	2	3	4	5	6	7	8	9	10	
43	112	124	43	163	135	147	00	145	100	5:17

1	2	3	4	5	6	7	8	9	10	
151	45	40	10	40	158	240	143	31	120	5:18

SHAPES PUZZLE

★ = 03   ✚ = 05

⚑ = 15

WORD PROBLEM

	LEMON	SUGAR	CUPS
TOTAL	193	854	654

1 cup	2 cups	3 cups	4 cups	5 cups
8 cents	16	24	32	40
6 cups	7 cups	8 cups	9 cups	10 c
48	56	64	72	80

WORD SEARCH

					G	E	C	K	O		
			Z			R					S
	G	O	O	S	E	A		L	I	O	N
				B	E	A	V	E	R	E	O
O	S	T	R	I	C	H	R		F		W
				A	B	A	T	F			D
	L	E	M	A	C		A	P	E		O
	Y			O		R					G
	N		O		T	I	G	E	R		
O	X	N			G	W	E	A	S	E	L

10 cups	20	30	40	50	60	70	80	90	100
80 cents	160 c	240 c	320 c	400 c	480 c	560 c	640 c	720 c	800 c

100 cents	200 cents	300 cents	400 cents	500 cents	600 cents	700 cents	800 cents
1 dollar	2 dollars	3 dollars	4 dollars	5 dollars	6 dollars	7 dollars	8 dollars

WEEK 6 – LESSON 6

1	2	3	4	5	6	7	8	
89	96	96	115	106	110	116	151	6:1

1	2	3	4	5	6	7	8	
86	114	264	263	165	175	169	160	6:2

1	2	3	4	5	6	7	8	
41	260	66	66	81	275	31	115	6:3

1	2	3	4	5	6	7	8	
201	41	166	33	20	41	311	495	6:4

1	2	3	4	5	6	7	8	
168	105	168	265	204	61	285	131	6:5

1	2	3	4	5	6	7	8	
165	21	188	13	62	71	314	201	6:6

1	2	3	4	5	6	7	8	
240	20	23	100	116	91	155	71	6:7

1	2	3	4	5	6	7	8	
182	147	79	81	158	154	411	144	6:8

1	2	3	4	5	6	7	8	
90	111	163	115	121	22	32	258	6:9

1	2	3	4	5	6	7	8	
175	76	23	61	95	122	335	161	6:10

1	2	3	4	5	6	7	8	
152	23	01	57	80	248	91	34	6:11

1	2	3	4	5	6	7	8	
141	186	35	150	72	323	260	211	6:12

LESSON 6 – MIND MATH PRACTICE WORK

1	2	3	4	5	6	7	8	9	10	
13	33	21	00	13	102	150	130	111	30	6:13

1	2	3	4	5	6	7	8	9	10	
39	00	61	100	160	210	71	13	155	111	6:14

1	2	3	4	5	6	7	8	9	10	
03	110	21	121	67	31	40	26	101	214	6:15

1	2	3	4	5	6	7	8	9	10	
61	101	111	210	10	40	113	65	130	81	6:16

1	2	3	4	5	6	7	8	9	10	
100	121	59	116	31	104	71	114	110	154	6:17

1	2	3	4	5	6	7	8	9	10	
133	96	162	69	80	103	143	175	170	110	6:18

SUDOKU

1	3	2	4
2	4	1	3
4	2	3	1
3	1	4	2

3	2	4	1
1	4	2	3
4	3	1	2
2	1	3	4

4	3	1	2
2	1	3	4
3	4	2	1
1	2	4	3

2	4	1	3
1	3	2	4
3	1	4	2
4	2	3	1

WEEK 7 – LESSON 7

1	2	3	4	5	6	7	8	
59	144	172	126	145	95	125	132	7:1

1	2	3	4	5	6	7	8	
66	64	77	243	69	68	60	21	7:2

1	2	3	4	5	6	7	8	
224	125	145	139	145	73	83	70	7:3

1	2	3	4	5	6	7	8	
79	80	158	152	252	22	153	269	7:4

1	2	3	4	5	6	7	8	
40	71	188	93	120	155	181	320	7:5

1	2	3	4	5	6	7	8	
154	111	70	33	230	102	122	201	7:6

1	2	3	4	5	6	7	8	
00	57	171	143	230	156	154	81	7:7

1	2	3	4	5	6	7	8	
154	186	35	142	125	340	452	501	7:8

1	2	3	4	5	6	7	8	
150	121	30	30	154	151	133	128	7:9

1	2	3	4	5	6	7	8	
252	52	252	123	100	240	153	422	7:10

1	2	3	4	5	6	7	8	
148	91	222	154	70	22	130	102	7:11

1	2	3	4	5	6	7	8	
87	252	154	20	305	352	141	552	7:12

LESSON 7 – MIND MATH PRACTICE WORK

1	2	3	4	5	6	7	8	9	10	
89	45	32	113	136	43	130	141	156	111	7:13

1	2	3	4	5	6	7	8	9	10	
86	55	144	152	122	122	121	100	116	152	7:14

1	2	3	4	5	6	7	8	9	10	
93	103	134	00	100	96	120	127	124	42	7:15

1	2	3	4	5	6	7	8	9	10	
63	12	161	144	114	75	40	136	122	152	7:16

1	2	3	4	5	6	7	8	9	10	
62	111	10	143	153	142	162	164	136	163	7:17

1	2	3	4	5	6	7	8	9	10	
63	158	162	172	112	140	127	100	62	132	7:18

SEPARATE SHAPES

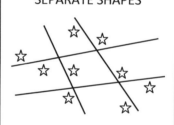

	Kangaroo Jo 9 feet per jump	Kangaroo Ben 8 feet per jump	Kangaroo Su 7 feet per jump
1st Jump	9	8	7
2nd Jump	18	16	14
3rd Jump	27	24	21
4th Jump	36	32	28
5th Jump	45	40	35
6th Jump	54	48	42
7th Jump	63	56	49
8th Jump	72	64	56
9th Jump	81	72	63
10th Jump	90	80	70
11th Jump	99	88	77
12th Jump		96	84
13th Jump			91
14th Jump			98
TOTAL	**99**	**96**	**98**

WEEK 8 – SKILL BUILDING

1	2	3	4	5	6	7	8	
92	17	74	252	02	236	433	202	8:1

1	2	3	4	5	6	7	8	
43	68	60	40	167	153	292	134	8:2

1	2	3	4	5	6	7	8	
93	100	103	153	121	90	162	273	8:3

1	2	3	4	5	6	7	8	
108	93	121	84	75	103	100	257	8:4

1	2	3	4	5	6	7	8	
53	53	60	102	83	00	120	131	8:5

1	2	3	4	5	6	7	8	
92	00	140	20	05	49	40	353	8:6

1	2	3	4	5	6	7	8	
44	117	78	50	23	152	333	331	8:7

1	2	3	4	5	6	7	8	
30	105	86	73	231	70	188	102	8:8

1	2	3	4	5	6	7	8	
66	131	77	227	69	154	45	21	8:9

1	2	3	4	5	6	7	8	
79	80	154	149	121	152	32	265	8:10

WEEK 8 – MIND MATH PRACTICE WORK

1	2	3	4	5	6	7	8	9	10	
67	43	88	22	80	142	72	113	138	101	8:11

1	2	3	4	5	6	7	8	9	10	
89	62	172	120	00	11	134	65	46	83	8:12

1	2	3	4	5	6	7	8	9	10	
42	77	162	23	122	92	43	102	202	00	8:13

1	2	3	4	5	6	7	8	9	10	
111	21	64	57	00	97	60	30	112	74	8:14

1	2	3	4	5	6	7	8	9	10	
33	51	20	50	112	140	151	62	74	41	8:15

1	2	3	4	5	6	7	8	9	10	
62	30	20	43	232	52	40	124	93	65	8:16

SEPARATE SHAPES

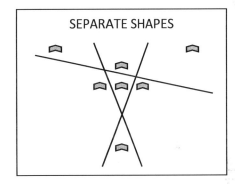

WORD SEARCH

		D	E	H	S	I	L	P	M	O	C	C	**A**
	W	E		L	U	F	L	L	**I**	K	**S**		E
		O	C				**E**		N			**D**	L
	E	N	N				X		C	**G**		E	B
	N	D	E				C		R	I		C	**A**
	I	E	I	E	L	B	**A**	E		E	F		E	P
	F	R	R					L		D	T		N	A
		F	E					L		I	E		T	**C**
	S	U	P	E	R	B		E		B	D			
		L	X					N		L				
		E					T	R	E	P	X		**E**	

SAI Speed Math Academy

Pg 93

1	2	3	4	5	6	7	8	
28	85	86	100	150	65	101	165	9:1

1	2	3	4	5	6	7	8	
117	100	165	185	206	242	164	163	9:2

1	2	3	4	5	6	7	8	
130	40	140	12	156	42	245	110	9:3

1	2	3	4	5	6	7	8	
140	00	179	110	163	180	241	657	9:4

1	2	3	4	5	6	7	8	
173	150	205	108	260	145	165	134	9:5

1	2	3	4	5	6	7	8	
135	124	268	94	44	307	40	114	9:6

1	2	3	4	5	6	7	8	
110	61	152	263	80	154	31	123	9:7

1	2	3	4	5	6	7	8	
60	43	107	190	141	190	000	405	9:8

1	2	3	4	5	6	7	8	
142	264	83	95	35	167	84	40	9:9

1	2	3	4	5	6	7	8	
138	89	76	152	160	10	234	250	9:10

1	2	3	4	5	6	7	8	
50	90	195	40	140	150	100	92	9:11

1	2	3	4	5	6	7	8	
46	45	151	190	40	40	42	56	9:12

LESSON 8 – MIND MATH PRACTICE WORK

1	2	3	4	5	6	7	8	9	10	
00	100	33	20	100	114	114	104	130	110	9:13

1	2	3	4	5	6	7	8	9	10	
50	100	150	200	04	163	22	30	200	54	9:14

1	2	3	4	5	6	7	8	9	10	
30	40	110	120	95	03	144	44	21	120	9:15

1	2	3	4	5	6	7	8	9	10	
65	24	174	114	04	01	30	170	140	80	9:16

1	2	3	4	5	6	7	8	9	10	
94	00	205	40	103	20	153	200	101	105	9:17

1	2	3	4	5	6	7	8	9	10	
02	104	111	110	123	155	03	10	170	32	9:18

SHAPES SUKODU

WEEK 10 – LESSON 9

1	2	3	4	5	6	7	8	
86	44	23	44	101	140	147	100	10:1

1	2	3	4	5	6	7	8	
223	22	134	165	155	135	134	00	10:2

1	2	3	4	5	6	7	8	
24	110	82	132	123	54	123	41	10:3

1	2	3	4	5	6	7	8	
185	219	134	155	154	112	153	131	10:4

1	2	3	4	5	6	7	8	
203	40	125	121	120	50	141	124	10:5

1	2	3	4	5	6	7	8	
128	144	140	71	93	102	350	153	10:6

1	2	3	4	5	6	7	8	
177	282	116	151	40	40	231	124	10:7

1	2	3	4	5	6	7	8	
115	133	94	120	145	151	291	10	10:8

1	2	3	4	5	6	7	8	
195	164	143	253	144	52	66	20	10:9

1	2	3	4	5	6	7	8	
198	00	110	142	00	352	453	564	10:10

1	2	3	4	5	6	7	8	
241	70	153	251	250	214	88	131	10:11

1	2	3	4	5	6	7	8	
80	253	30	100	251	253	210	123	10:12

LESSON 9 – MIND MATH PRACTICE WORK

1	2	3	4	5	6	7	8	9	10	
59	95	68	61	101	150	141	126	141	100	10:13

1	2	3	4	5	6	7	8	9	10	
159	103	180	132	124	41	123	154	143	138	10:14

1	2	3	4	5	6	7	8	9	10	
50	101	83	102	120	144	40	104	44	141	10:15

1	2	3	4	5	6	7	8	9	10	
64	53	133	152	141	100	120	01	42	198	10:16

1	2	3	4	5	6	7	8	9	10	
69	10	173	203	144	44	154	00	124	143	10:17

1	2	3	4	5	6	7	8	9	10	
00	00	110	155	111	163	13	44	101	101	10:18

SEPARATE SHAPES

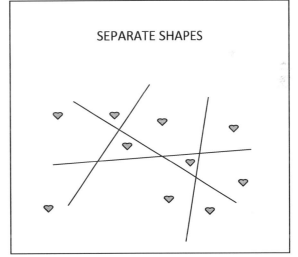

ABOUT SAI SPEED MATH ACADEMY

One subject that is very important for success in this world, along with being able to read and write, is the knowledge of numbers. Math is one subject which requires proficiency from anyone who wants to achieve something in life. A strong foundation and a basic understanding of math is a must to mastering higher levels of math.

We, the family, best friends, and parents of children in elementary school, early on discovered that what our children were learning at school was not enough for them to master the basics of math. Teachers at school, with the resources they had, did the best they could. But, as parents, we had to do more to help them understand the relationship between numbers and basic functions of adding, subtracting, multiplying and dividing. Also, what made us cringe is the fact that our children's attitude towards more complex math was to say, "Oh, we are allowed to use a calculator in class". This did not sit well with us. Even though we did not have a specific system that we followed, each of us could do basic calculations in our minds without looking for a calculator. So, this made us want to do more for our children.

We started to look into the various methods that were available in the marketplace to help our children understand basic math and reduce their dependency on calculators. We came across soroban, a wonderful calculating tool from Japan. Soroban perfectly fits with the base-10 number system used at present and provides a systematic method to follow while calculating in one's mind.

This convinced us and within a short time we were able to work with fluency on the tool. The next step was to introduce it to our children, which we thought was going to be an easy task. It, however, was not. It was next to impossible to find the resources or the curriculum to help us introduce the tool in the correct order. Teaching all the concepts in one sitting and expecting children to apply them to the set of problems we gave them only made them push away the tool in frustration.

However, help comes to those who ask, and to those who are willing to work to achieve their goals. We came across a soroban teacher who helped us by giving us ideas and an outline of how soroban should be introduced. But, we still needed an actual worksheet to give our children to practice on. That is when we decided to come up with practice worksheets of our own design for our kids.

Slowly and steadily, practicing with the worksheets that we developed, our children started to get the idea and loved what they could do with a soroban. Soon we realized that they were better with mind math than we were.

Today, 6 years later, all our kids have completed their soroban training and are reaping the benefits of the hard work that they did over the years.

Now, although very happy, we were humbled at the number of requests we got from parents who wanted to know more about our curriculum. We had no way to share our new knowledge with them.

Now, through the introduction of our instruction book and workbooks, that has changed. We want to share everything we know with all the dedicated parents who are interested in teaching soroban to their children. This is our humble attempt to bring a systematic instruction manual and corresponding workbook to help introduce your children to soroban.

What started as a project to help our kids has grown over the years and we are fortunate to say that a number of children have benefitted learning with the same curriculum that we developed for our children.

Thank you for choosing our system to enhance your children's mathematical skills.

We love working on soroban and hope you do too!

List of SAI Speed Math Academy Publications

LEVEL – 1

 Abacus Mind Math Instruction Book Level – 1: Step by Step Guide to Excel at Mind Math with Soroban, a Japanese Abacus
ISBN-13: 978-1941589007

 Abacus Mind Math Level – 1 Workbook 1 of 2: Excel at Mind Math with Soroban, a Japanese Abacus
ISBN-13: 978-1941589014

 Abacus Mind Math Level – 1 Workbook 2 of 2: Excel at Mind Math with Soroban, a Japanese Abacus
ISBN-13: 978-1941589021

LEVEL – 2

 Abacus Mind Math Instruction Book Level – 2: Step by Step Guide to Excel at Mind Math with Soroban, a Japanese Abacus
ISBN-13: 978-1941589038

 Abacus Mind Math Level – 2 Workbook 1 of 2: Excel at Mind Math with Soroban, a Japanese Abacus
ISBN-13: 978-1941589045

 Abacus Mind Math Level – 2 Workbook 2 of 2: Excel at Mind Math with Soroban, a Japanese Abacus
ISBN-13: 978-1941589052

LEVEL – 3

 Abacus Mind Math Instruction Book Level – 3: Step by Step Guide to Excel at Mind Math with Soroban, a Japanese Abacus
ISBN-13: 9781941589069

 Abacus Mind Math Level – 3 Workbook 1 of 2: Excel at Mind Math with Soroban, a Japanese Abacus
ISBN-13: 9781941589076

 Abacus Mind Math Level – 3 Workbook 2 of 2: Excel at Mind Math with Soroban, a Japanese Abacus
ISBN-13: 9781941589083

Continued.....

Not Related To The Abacus Mind Math Series Books

Learn To Do MATH WITH SOROBAN, a Japanese Abacus

ISBN-13: 978-1-5371-6329-1

Made in the USA
Las Vegas, NV
17 March 2022

45846760R00061